# British
# Forests

# British Forests

The Forestry
Commission
1919–2019

General Editor Ian Gambles

PROFILE
EDITIONS

Contributors

*Edited by:*
Ian Gambles

*With contributions from:*
Helen Connor-Walton
Katherine Deeks
Mark Durk
Louise Fleetwood
Peter Freer-Smith
Paddy Harrop
Richard Howe
Gary Kerr
PK Khaira-Creswell
Brian Mahony
Bill Mason
Josh Roberts
Hayley Skipper
Jonathan Spencer
Sir Henry Studholme
Chris Quine
Ruth Wilson

First published in Great Britain in 2019 by
Profile Editions, an imprint of
PROFILE BOOKS LTD
29 Cloth Fair
London
ECIA 7NN
*www.profileeditions.com*

10 9 8 7 6 5 4 3 2 1

Design and cartography by James Alexander/Jade Design
using Adobe Caslon Pro and Big Caslon

Printed and bound in Great Britain by Gomer

A CIP catalogue record for this book is available
from the British Library.

ISBN 978 1 78816 313 2

FSC
www.fsc.org

MIX
Paper from
responsible sources
FSC® C114687

# CONTENTS

# Foreword

---

Growing up as a child amid the oaks and ash trees of the Sussex Weald, for me, the Forestry Commission ranks with the NHS and the Houses of Parliament as key to our British way of life. For 100 years it has overseen the preservation, support and development of the woodlands and forests of our green and pleasant land.

Today I am Chair of one of Britain's newest wooded areas – the Heart of England Forest in Warwickshire. We have already embarked upon planting some 30,000 acres of native woodlands – tomorrow's 'new forest'. In this considerable task, the Forestry Commission's enthusiasm, support, advice and assistance is proving invaluable.

This wonderful book describes the Commission's evolution over its first 100 years, but, amid the vastly increased need for more trees in Britain, for timber, and to help combat climate change and tree diseases, the Forestry Commission continues to play an absolutely indispensable role. It is rightly proud of its first century of achievement but mindful of the massive challenges ahead.

The next 100 years will prove the greatest undertaking yet. Sustaining our existing trees and woodland and planting more, on an unprecedented scale, will find the woodsmen, the foresters and those who guide them in the Forestry Commission at the very forefront of that work. But, as this book reveals, they have done it before: after the needs of the First World War devastated our tree stock, it was the Commission that led the campaign to replant. I confess that I am proud indeed of the Forestry Commission's vital role in investing so profoundly not only in the past, but in all our futures.

*Jon Snow*

# Introduction

From Domesday in 1086 to the end of the Great War in 1918, England lost two-thirds of its forests. The determination to arrest and reverse that long decline right across Britain led in 1919 to the creation of the Forestry Commission, setting in train 100 years of resurgence. In that remarkable century, woodland cover has doubled, a modern timber industry has grown from nothing, and the British people have built a new relationship with the forests and the life within them. This book celebrates that century of change and the men and women who made it happen.

Part I tells the story of that time, revealing how fast human history changes compared with the slow life of the trees. What began as a single-minded drive to restore strategic timber supplies denuded for pit-props and trench boards in war, evolved through periods of dramatic and sometimes ruthless landscape transformation into an entirely new culture of multipurpose forestry, caring for wildlife, giving people air and space, and supporting a complex economy. From its earliest days as a large and hierarchical department of the British government, employing and often housing many thousands of men to plant the new forests, the Commission has formed the foundations of a diverse and open forestry environment, with new organisations managing the public forests in England, Scotland and Wales; a flowering of professionalism embracing silviculture, ecology, engineering, recreation and the arts; and a thriving private sector both in forestry and in wood processing.

Part II looks in more depth at some of the most important issues in British forestry today. Invasive species, pests and diseases continue to menace our woodlands, and forestry stands on the front line of climate

8

change – even the fastest growing trees we plant today will reach maturity when the world is warmer. The science and skills of planning and growing the forests have deep roots in the Forestry Commission, and keep developing to meet fresh challenges. With greater understanding of the value of our natural environment has come a new emphasis on stewardship and restoration of precious habitats. And as the forest has opened to the people, and human artistic expression has found its way into the woods, so the dense conurbations where most of us now live have themselves begun to welcome the urban forest, the lungs of the city.

Part III travels around Britain to introduce some of the wonderful public forests in the care of Forestry England, Forestry and Land Scotland, and Natural Resources Wales. All of them are open, day and night, all seasons round. They are our shared inheritance.

This book has been written entirely by past and present Forestry Commission people. Our hope is to share with readers something of the story of British forestry over the last 100 years, including why the Commission came into being and how it grew and changed, why it and its successor bodies in England, Scotland and Wales are important today, and some of the fascinating work we do and the challenges we face. We hope it will also invite you in, to visit and enjoy the nations' forests, to see and explore more.

This is a story of people as much as a story of trees. Our forests were created by the labour and love of many who spent their whole working lives with the Forestry Commission, and this book is dedicated to the memory of all those who have gone before. Constantly evolving to meet the changing needs of a changing world, their achievement survives them, and will survive us all.

*Ian Gambles*

Forest

In fact, the trees are murmuring under your feet,
a buried empathy; you tread it.
                              High over your head,
the canopy sieves light; a conversation
you lip-read. The forest
                         keeps different time;
slow hours as long as your life,
so you feel human.

So you feel more human; persuaded what you are
by wordless breath of wood, reason in resin.
You might name them –
                      oak, ash, holly, beech, elm –
but the giants are silence alive, superior,
and now you are all instinct;
swinging the small lamp of your heart
as you venture their world:

the green, shadowy, garlic air
                          your ancestors breathed.
Ah, you thought love human
till you lost yourself in the forest,
but it is more strange.
                      These grave and patient saints
who pray and pray
and suffer your little embrace.

*Carol Ann Duffy*

Commissioned to mark the Forestry Commission's centenary

# Beginnings

As the clouds of dust settled after what people believed had been the war to end all wars, Great Britain finally had the chance to rebuild, restock and reorganise. There was not only an enthusiasm for a return to normal life, but also an appetite for change. The war had had an enormous impact on Britain which was to be felt for decades to come. Around 700,000 British soldiers had died and, of those who returned, hundreds of thousands had been injured both mentally and physically. The vast numbers of returning soldiers required work in an economy no longer buoyed up by the investment of war, while women saw their matrimonial prospects decline but their opportunities to work increase, and the resettlement of the European map had changed the landscapes of politics and trade. Britain had to find ways to cover the huge cost of the war and to heal its wounds, but the nation also found itself with pressing issues to tackle. The war had shone a new political light on some pre-war concerns which the government now had to face. These included not only women's suffrage, but also the poor state of the nation's forests, and the need for the government to reverse the millennia-old deforestation of the British landscape and engage in the large-scale creation of forests.

The deforestation had been a long process. Britain was under ice sheets when the last ice age ended nearly 12,000 years ago. As the ice retreated, trees returned via a land bridge with continental Europe – tentatively at first with pioneer species like birch, pine, juniper and willow, but over about 4,000 years 35 or so other species arrived, determining our native palette of trees before the rising sea level made Britain an island. With these arrived birds and insects and mammals, creating a whole woodland ecology that covered perhaps 60 per cent of the land. How much was wooded is debated but what is sure is that when Neolithic farmers arrived about 5,000 years ago, they began the process of clearing this fertile island – a process that accelerated with the discovery of first bronze and then iron technologies to build better tools for felling the forest. By the time the Romans invaded, their writers were able to describe a well-farmed and largely deforested land. One thousand years after this, when a later invader commissioned the Domesday Book, forest cover was perhaps 15 per cent in England – cover that continued to be seriously eroded for more than two centuries as populations grew rapidly and as a consequence land was needed for food, and timber was extracted for building and heating. It was only after 1350 when the bubonic plague reduced the population by perhaps half over two centuries, and trade to meet the country's timber needs developed with the Baltic, that the forest area stabilised. Even so, by the time of the agricultural survey of 1877 when traditional forestry in England had become unviable, the area of trees in Britain had shrunk to less than 4 per cent of the land area.

The outbreak of the First World War exposed the country's vulnerability to disruption of its timber supplies. Around 90 per cent of the timber being used in Britain was being imported – much of it from the Baltic, overwhelmingly from Russia, as well as from the Empire's forests, which included the forests of Canada and India. Additionally timber consumption had soared in the years leading up to war. With war declared, not only was timber needed urgently for the war effort but also trade had been disrupted, not least by the new German fleet of submarines – the U-boats that from October 1914 began to attack British merchant shipping. This left the country in a very precarious situation and focused political minds on what was a much-depleted and undermanaged home-grown timber resource. It is estimated that as many as a third of the trees of Britain had to be felled during the First World War to keep up with the resulting demand for timber.

Timber was critical to the war effort from its use as duckboards in the trenches and pit-props for the mines to providing essential raw materials for packaging or building. The massive shortage of timber transformed a concern of rural enthusiasts, who were easy to ignore, into a mainstream political issue. Ideas that had been the prerogative of foresters now began to be discussed at Westminster and appeared prescient rather than irrelevant.

The State had long been involved in forestry. Indeed, some of Britain's oldest possessions are the Norman-created Royal forests and for centuries monarchs, commissions and learned societies had been advocating increased forestation. However, before the formation of the Forestry Commission in 1919 the management of State woodland assets had been inconsistent. Outside the State forests, the long-time scales of forestry and the more pressing and immediate demands of the rural population had tended to reduce rather than increase the area of forest. This was especially true after 1862. In that year naval shipbuilding changed forever following the naval battle of Hampton Roads during the American Civil War, in which the Confederate ironclad vessel CSS *Virginia* effortlessly sank the Union wooden frigates USS *Congress* and USS *Cumberland*. Shock waves were felt as far away as London as admirals brought up on wooden ships realised that all future warships would have to be ironclad. State interest in forests waned. No longer were Britain's majestic oak trees in demand to supply the 'wooden walls' of the navy. The patriotic imperative to plant oak trees that had been encouraged by Evelyn and Nelson was no more. By 1870 over five times more tonnage of iron ships – even excluding warships – than of wooden-hulled vessels was being launched.

Over the centuries there had been occasional bursts of enthusiasm from kings and parliaments to plant and manage trees within the Royal forests, but there was inadequate clear direction or vision to ensure long term and consistent good management. For private owners, economic markets that supported traditional forest management had faltered in the 19th century. The boom years of British agriculture from 1840 to 1875 drove an expansion of farmland for food production, which encouraged the removal of forests on areas with good soil. This boom collapsed in the final quarter of the 19th century under a flood of cheap corn from Canada and the United States, as well as frozen meat from Australasia and South America. However, the damage had been done and left the countryside impoverished, as described so hauntingly by Thomas Hardy. In addition Britain was not well able to provide a market for the output of its outmoded and fragmented forests, especially when timber could be cheaply and easily imported. Despite the enthusiasm of many landowners for planting, the area under forest in Britain was recorded as only 885,000 hectares or 4 per cent of the land area by the time of the 1877 Agricultural Census.

The area of woodland may have diminished but much of the experimentation and research that led to the later expansion of forestry was already under way in the 19th century. During the early part of the century the great plant hunters like David Douglas and John Veitch were bringing new species into the UK and landowners were experimenting in arboreta such as at Westonbirt – first established in 1829 by Robert Holford and now managed for the nation by the Forestry Commission – and new plantations such as the Duke of Athol's larch plantations at Dunkeld. The successes as well as failures of these plantings gave future generations an understanding of what trees were available for planting and how they would perform in Great Britain. These were an essential backdrop to the work of the country's Royal Arboricultural Societies, who lobbied passionately for afforestation in Britain.

### Royal Societies

The Scottish Arboricultural Society was founded in 1854. It was permitted to add the prefix 'Royal' in 1887. The English followed suit and the English Arboricultural Society was established in 1882, obtaining a Royal Charter in 1905. It was only in 1930, 11 years after the creation of the Forestry Commission, that the Scottish renamed their association the Royal Scottish Forestry Society; in the following year the English name changed to the Royal English Forestry Society, which later became the Royal Forestry Society of England, Wales and Northern Ireland.

The lessons of the war were multilayered: they brought into sharp focus what the learned societies and silviculturalists had been saying for decades about timber supplies, but they also intensified Britain's sense of social responsibility. Officers and men bound together in the appalling conditions of trench warfare returned home changed. Not only was there work to find for demobbed soldiers, but there was a real desire to relieve the poverty and depopulation of the rural areas that many were returning to. None of this could be delivered by the mechanisms available before the war. However, the war effort had mobilised an army and a societal endeavour on a scale never seen before. This provided direct experience of large-scale projects that were centrally organised and led, and inspired a new vision of what might be achieved if the State involved itself in land management. A well-funded and centralised government body with long-term objectives could achieve what no single landowner or group of landowners could, both by giving clarity of direction and by creating the necessary forestry skills on a large scale.

Another fundamental reason behind the need for a centralised organisation to oversee forestry was simply that no one knew much about what was really happening. The exact figures for timber production or planting were not available; nor was any other data. During the war years any attempted calculation involving the timber reserves was liable to be wildly inaccurate. In 1916 when attention was properly turned to home-grown timber, it became clear, as George Ryle so aptly pointed out, that the newly formed Timber Supplies Department 'had no nucleus upon which to build' given the lack of information available to it.

The Timber Supplies Department ran for three years until 1919. Through its work, 182,000 hectares (a very significant portion of the

*Loading charcoal sacks onto cart, Forest of Dean, 1909–12*

country's timber reserves and virtually all its softwood resource) was identified and felled for the war effort. Home production rose from under 1 million tons before the war to 4.5 million tons in 1918. While it left the country denuded of forests, a positive side of its legacy was as the source and proving ground of many future members of the Forestry Commission. At this time forestry was a highly labour-intensive business with people and horses needed to carry out every part of the process. Even when tractors or machinery could be found they were in very short supply because, in terms of the many types of war work taking place, forestry was not at the top of the list of priorities. As a result the burden fell almost entirely on the shoulders of the hard-working men and women who joined the war effort. By 1918 it is believed that as many as 15,000 people were being used as part of the forestry effort – many supplied by the Canadian Forestry Corps, the Newfoundland Forestry Corps and significantly by our own newly created Women's Forestry Service (WFS).

Alongside this essential practical work a political dimension emerged that would change forever the political landscape of forestry. In July 1916 Prime Minister Herbert Henry Asquith created the Forestry Sub-Committee of the Ministry of Reconstruction, which he instructed to consider the lessons learnt from the experience of forestry during the war years, and to use them to inform the future by discussing the best means of solving them. The Sub-Committee reported back to Asquith in 1917 with findings and suggestions which went on to inform forest policy for decades afterwards. The group was chaired by Francis Dyke (later Sir Francis) Acland MP, a member of a Devon landowning family. The Acland family had strong Liberal traditions, which Francis shared. His father was a Liberal MP, as had been his uncle Sir Thomas Acland, 12th Baronet, who in 1917 made a bequest of over 3,000 hectares of his north Devon estate Holnicote to the National Trust for 500 years – nearly doubling the area of the young organisation. Francis's wife, Eleanor, was an active suffragist, a founder in 1913 of the Liberal Women's Suffrage Union, and in 1929 she was elected president of the Women's Liberal Federation. Francis, who went on to serve as one of the first Commissioners, had a political vision to create an asset for the nation and was able to assemble a remarkable sub-committee with real expertise in forestry: Professor Schlich, Lord Lovat and Sir John Stirling

Maxwell (discussed in more detail on p.19); Lord Clinton, Secretary of the Board of Agriculture; and Roy Robinson, then 33, an Australian Rhodes Scholar who had studied under Schlich. The Sub-Committee provided the first four Chairmen of the Commission who would guide the organisation for over 30 years.

The findings of the Acland-chaired Sub-Committee led directly to the government's decision to create the Forestry Commission in 1919. There was support for this in the House of Commons as well as the House of Lords, and the Commission officially came into being on 1 September 1919 with the passing of the Forestry Act. The new organisation had eight Commissioners, and it had been agreed that these would include one with technical forestry knowledge, at least two who had experience of forestry in Scotland, and one would act as Chairman.

## Forestry Commissions in Other Countries

By 1919 forestry was a global issue and Britain did not go into the process of establishing a new forestry body blindly. While during the 19th century woods may have been falling out of management in Great Britain, that was not the case throughout the Empire or in Europe. As early as the 1850s the government of India had begun to understand the need to protect forests and coordinate their management. It looked to France and Germany as having older and active traditions of forest management and established forestry training, and in 1864 the German-born Dietrich Brandis was appointed inspector general of forests in India. It was an inspired choice. Brandis was an extraordinary man with exceptional intelligence, energy and vision who developed a scientific approach to managing forests and founded the Imperial Forest School in Dehradun. His successor in the role, William Schlich, went on to become in 1885 professor of forestry at Cooper's Hill, a college to train foresters for work throughout the Empire. When this closed in 1906, he founded the Forestry Programme at Oxford University. Schlich was hugely influential. Not only was he a member of the Acland Sub-Committee but his works on forestry and afforestation were to provide intellectual bedrock to the creation of the Forestry Commission.

The ideas of both Brandis and Schlich had been highly influential not just in India and the wider British Empire but also on Gifford Pinchot in the United States who became the first chief of the US Forest Service when it was founded in 1905. A sense of international concern over forests was present even as the British Forestry Commission was formed. The Acland Sub-Committee had been worried about over-exploitation of the forests of Canada and one of the first acts of the young Commission was the convening of an Empire Forestry Conference in 1920, drawing to London foresters from around the world.

The 16th Lord Lovat was the first Chairman of the Forestry Commission and was extraordinarily well qualified for the task, having had first-hand experience of the timber supply problems that led to its creation. He had been the general in charge of supplying the British Army – and sometimes also the French Army – with timber from French forests during the last two years of the war. This had been a vast operation. By the end of the war the division employed 45,000 men – 63 Companies of the Canadian Forestry Corps, 11 Royal Engineer Forestry Companies – as well as 6,000 horses and 1,000 motorised vehicles. On Lovat's appointment in April 1917 only 50,000 tons of timber a month were reaching the British Army, but during the 20 months from April 2017 to the end of the war he delivered 3 million tons of timber to the British, French and Americans and built up a reserve of a further 700,000 tons. To his contemporaries Simon, 16th Lord Lovat and 22nd Chief of the Clan Fraser, was a remarkable character. He was an Oxford-educated soldier who had raised the Lovat Scouts regiment to use the skills of Highland gillies in observing deer as specialists for reconnaissance during the Boer War. These units became the sniper (sharpshooter) regiments in the First World War. Lord Lovat had an exemplary war record both in the Boer War and the First World War but after contracting dysentery at Gallipoli he was not deemed medically fit for the front line and was therefore put in command of the timber supply to the army. In spite of his probable, but characteristically unexpressed, disappointment in being taken away from active service it was an inspired posting. The role required knowledge of soldiering and forest management, strong leadership to command Canadian foresters, and immense charm and tact to negotiate with the French. All of these things Lord Lovat possessed in spades. In negotiating with the French he succeeded admirably and received the *Légion d'honneur* and – something which amused him exceedingly – the *Ordre du Mérite agricole*.

In addition to his remarkable war record Lord Lovat brought his impeccable social and political connections to the newly formed Forestry Commission. When the Geddes Axe (the massive 1922 cutting of government expenditure) threatened to fell the young Commission, Lovat's friendship with a number of men in the Cabinet allowed the organisation to survive – albeit trimmed down. In 1925, facing further cuts from an incoming Tory administration, Lovat's conversations with Winston Churchill, the Chancellor of the Exchequer, may have saved the Commission a second time. He shot with the Royal Family at Sandringham and gambled with the socialites at Monte Carlo, once winning £3,554 in a single evening (the equivalent of around £350,000 today).

Lord Lovat had inherited his family estate in Scotland after his father's early death when he was only 16, making him not only a major Scottish landowner, but also one of the youngest. The estate was heavily mortgaged when he inherited it, in part as a result of his father's rebuilding of the main house Beaufort during the closing years of the Victorian agricultural boom. This encouraged Lovat to take a keen interest in the problems of owning and managing land. In the years before the First World War he had worked with Sir John Stirling Maxwell, later to be not only one of the first Commissioners but also its third Chairman, in developing forestry schemes in Scotland. He felt all his life a sense of responsibility for his property, and also an interest and sympathy for the economic challenges faced by remote rural areas in Scotland – a sense of the need to care for people ran deep within him. It was this background and experience that he would bring to the first decade of the new Forestry Commission.

Lovat was styled the 'Father of the Forestry Commission' by George Ryle who credited him with the successful establishment of the Commission during the early years. Every afternoon at 4pm on the dot he presided over afternoon tea sessions with his staff, his private secretary pouring out the tea. Lovat secretly put aside a sum of money every year during his Chairmanship to be used for any foresters or their families who fell upon hard times. Two subsequent Chairmen added to it and many years later it was officially recognised as the Forestry Commission Benevolent Fund. Equally visionary was his desire to involve all political parties in the forestry debate. He appointed Walter Smith MP, the former president of the National Union of Agricultural Workers, as the first Labour Commissioner in 1925.

The first Forestry Commissioners were appointed on 29 November and held their first meeting on 7 December. As soon as the key matters had been discussed, Lord Lovat set off for Scotland by train to plant the first tree. However, in this he was frustrated. His fellow Commissioner, the Devon-based Lord Clinton, was equally determined to plant the first ever Forestry Commission tree and, with a shorter journey, arrived later that day at Eggesford to be met by enthusiastic local foresters who drove him off to Flashdown Wood, where he planted beech and larch saplings. Lovat's journey by sleeper train was all the way to the north of Scotland and consequently somewhat longer. Despite rushing off for the train, poor Lord Lovat was met the next day at Elgin Station not only by his forester but also by a telegram from his rival, announcing that the first tree had already been planted the previous evening. Tactfully the official record lists the first trees as being both planted in England and in Scotland on 8 December 1919. Lord Clinton later succeeded Lord Lovat and became the second Chairman of the Commission.

The scope of work bestowed on the Forestry Commission by the Forestry Act was vast. It was founded with three clear aims: to reduce the quantity of timber being imported; to ensure a reserve of standing timber for use in a future crisis such as another war; and lastly to reduce the decline of the rural population across Britain. The Commission had responsibilities and duties connected not just with State-owned woodlands, but also with privately held woods. The First World War had shown that the government was not well enough informed about the forest industry in Britain, and by granting these additional powers to the Commission it sought to introduce a measure of regulation. As a result the Commission could take action against landowners who failed to control the population of rabbits, squirrels and vermin in the woods. The organisation could also grant or loan money to private individuals as well as local authorities for the purpose of afforestation and replanting.

The establishment of forest industries was included in the remit. The Forestry Act even sanctioned several branches of in-house work including publication, training and research forestry. While the majority of publications were intended for an industry audience, and included guides on technical aspects of silviculture, this very book can trace its origins to the Act and its far-reaching decision to encourage publication within the organisation. Anniversary books were published to celebrate the 50th and 75th anniversaries of the Forestry Commission as well, so this book happily continues that tradition.

All woodland owned by the State fell under the management of the Commission, but in order to fulfil its brief of sizeable afforestation the acquisition of land was of immediate importance in those early years. During the first year of its existence, a grand total of 19,551 hectares was purchased by the Commissioners. However, acquiring land was only the beginning for in order to create new woodlands a great deal of work was necessary. Not only did the land need to be prepared for planting, but suitable saplings needed to be sourced or even grown, wildlife had to be kept under control while saplings were growing, and skilled foresters to carry out this work had to be found. It must be remembered that the

*Horse ploughing. Two-horse plough on the Lon Mor, Highland, 1927*

forestry industry in 1919 was not the efficient, well-staffed and educated sector it is today. Starting almost from scratch as far as Britain was concerned, the Forestry Commission was instrumental in the formation of the forestry industry as we now know it, possessed of high-tech machinery, forestry colleges, tree nurseries and scientific knowledge.

The first year of any new pursuit is inevitably one of struggle and challenge, yet also one of great passion and drive. The Commission was no exception and, thanks to its determination, within the first year alone an enormous amount of work had been achieved, including the establishment of policies, hiring of staff, strengthening of forest training and 645 hectares of planting on Commission land. These were impressive achievements considering the mere 12 months' passage, and set the scene for the hard-working ethic of the organisation.

In 1924 most of the forests of the Crown Estate became part of the Commission. The once extensive Royal forests which had been in public ownership for nearly 900 years, like the New Forest and the Forest of Dean, had by then been sadly depleted to just 48,967 hectares. To this day, these forests retain distinctive administrative structures dating back to the Middle Ages. Not only did the fledgling organisation inherit these Royal Forests,, but also Hafod Fawr in Wales, which HM's Officer for Woods had acquired in 1899 for the purposes of experimenting with upland plantation forestry and which provided early lessons for the Commission. Experiments with Sitka Spruce at Hafod Fawr made a deep impression on W.H. Guillebaud, the Commission's Research Officer in the 1920s, leading to its widespread adoption elsewhere. Inverliever, purchased in 1907, also provided valuable lessons in planting for the new foresters.

In 1923 the Irish Free State was formed, and the brief four years of the Forestry Commission in Ireland ended. In practice very little had been achieved there prior to this, although the Irish had already taken steps towards State forestry when in 1903 the Department of Agriculture and Technical Instruction (DATI) for Ireland bought woodland and established a training centre at Avondale House in Co. Wicklow. Afforestation was much needed. In 1908, the Departmental Committee on Irish Forestry estimated the area under forest in Ireland to be around 1.5 per cent of the total land area of the island, and fuel and timber shortages during the First World War only made this worse. Nevertheless the 1919 Forestry Act remained law in Ireland, and the Irish government itself began a similar programme to the Forestry Commission in 1923 that it accelerated from 1928.

## An Anecdote

The Forestry Commission, both then and now, is filled with colourful characters and many amusing little anecdotes. A memorable one from the early years involved the Secretary of the Commission who was well known for his stinginess over money. So tight was he where the office budget was concerned that he even claimed the headquarters could not afford a clock to let the staff know when to go home. As a result his enterprising colleagues clubbed together and bought a small alarm clock which they set for 5pm every day, and once the bell was ringing would slide it down from the top floor to just outside the Secretary's office on a long piece of string to announce the end of the working day. The poor man held out as long as he could, but eventually the loud ringing grew too much and he relented to the tune of a new office clock.

At the end of the first five years, in September 1924, the Commissioners could look back with some satisfaction at a great achievement. In the teeth of a recession a new organisation had been created, 56,656 hectares of new land had been acquired (purchased, leased or taken under management) of which 15,983 hectares had already been planted. The Forestry Commission now held 73 forests between England, Scotland and Wales and the old Royal forests had been taken in hand. Progress had also been demonstrated in other areas and with the proposed survey of British woodlands – something the war had so sharply reminded was necessary – almost complete, a scientific arm of the Commission had commenced work and was making great strides. Additionally, the Commission had encouraged and participated in two Empire Forestry Conferences. Despite the landscape of financial and political uncertainty, the Forestry Commission had not only shown its worth, but also demonstrated its future potential.

This was a sound start. The years ahead would test the young organisation further, at times almost to breaking point, but the roots laid by Acland and his Sub-Committee were strong. Strong enough to allow us to be celebrating the 100th anniversary of a State forest service that, while it has changed and adapted to economic, social and environmental pressures, remains true to the principles and ideals of public service laid out over a century ago.

*Sir Henry Studholme and Ruth Wilson*

# One Hundred Years of the Forestry Commission

A century on it is all too easy to assume that the fledgling organisation formed in 1919 was always going to succeed, but in fact the Forestry Commission faced challenges from the very start. Today's organisation has many of the aims of the fledgling, but it has changed extraordinarily in that time, reflecting changes in the wider society of the 20th century. The Commission's immediate remit on foundation was the establishment of a timber reserve for the nation and, in its first three decades, to provide labouring work for the unemployed. As a department of government, it could acquire land, build its own roads and bridges on that land, and even create entire communities, sustaining housing, shops and occasionally local football teams in the remotest locations of the country. As the earliest planted forests came to maturity in the later part of the 1960s and the initial task was accomplished, priorities changed: there was a new focus on wildlife and the recreational use of forests. In the decades that followed, mechanisation and privatisation led to huge reductions in the workforce, an increasing emphasis on research, and the opening of the forests to the public. With the abandonment of proposals for privatisation at the start of this decade, the Commission has today become, rather like the forests that it manages, a national treasure that grows more complex, sustainable and interesting as it matures.

# The 1920s

Economically this decade was bookended by periods of financial depression and these created a challenging start for the Forestry Commission. Recession in 1920–21 was followed by a few years of prosperity until the devastating Great Depression in 1929–30. With government funding under the microscope, economic volatility threatened to end the great forestry endeavour before it had the chance to make an impact. The price of land varied alarmingly and the impact on forestry employees was significant. In Britain in the aftermath of the First World War a great deal of land changed hands: estates were broken up, tenant farmers were offered the chance to buy their farms, and parcels of woodland went to the highest bidder. The newly created Commission almost didn't survive this economic seesaw and its right to buy land was suspended for six long months in 1921 as the Treasury proposed that afforestation plans be scrapped. Foresters held their breath and waited, but thankfully this proved to be a minor blip. However, as imported food flooded the country and left the poorer farmers with large mortgages and small means of making a profit, the market for land crashed. Ironically it was this heavy blow to home-grown British farm produce that aided the establishment of home-grown British trees.

For many landowners, selling land to the Forestry Commission proved a way out of financial problems, though government did set limits on what it could purchase. For example, in 1922 the limit on the Commission's buying power was set at £3 per acre (0.4 hectare), effectively reducing it to buying poor land on which it was not possible to grow good-quality farm crops or keep dairy cattle. Thus started the balancing act, which still continues to this day, between the respective rights and merits of using the nation's land for agriculture or forestry. By the end of the decade the Great Depression had struck and no one seemed immune to its stranglehold. The seasonal nature of forestry work meant that some foresters were employed for only a couple of seasons of the year, while others were paid only when the weather allowed them to work. This left many short of money and, with prices high, staff endured a very hard time as they established the public forest estate.

## Creation of the New Timber Reserve

When it was set up in 1919, the Forestry Commission had been given a specific responsibility for the 'development of afforestation' in order to create the new reserve of mainly coniferous timber that was needed. The level of expectation and the scale of the challenge were massive and unprecedented. The Commission identified 1,618,743 hectares of 'waste land' as being of limited use for any other purpose. This was the nation's poorest agricultural land but was believed to be capable of growing first-class conifer timber similar to that being imported. Almost all of the mature coniferous timber had been felled from existing woodland, and in the depressed post-war economy most landowners were incapable of meeting the costs of the replanting that was urgently required.

The Forestry Commission started this immense task from scratch. Staff had to be recruited and trained, management bases established, and land surveyed and acquired in some of the most remote parts of the country. The most appropriate tree species had to be identified to survive and thrive on what were often initially very inhospitable sites. Many trees were planted on bleak, windswept uplands into dense grass or heather and sometimes among rocky screes. In the Ennerdale Valley in the Lake District, the trees were planted into soil that was brought up to the screes in panniers carried by ponies. Sources of seed had to be found and nurseries established to grow the plants to supply the ambitious planting programmes. Nursery techniques were developed to produce plants that could stand the transport and planting operations and survive when planted on the hill.

Cultivation methods had to be developed – ploughing and drainage using horses and crawler tractors (tractors on caterpillar tracks), or hand-cutting of turves – and fences had to be erected over many miles of arduous terrain to protect the newly planted trees from grazing livestock. The trees were carried in bags slung over the workers' shoulders and planted by hand using a spade or mattock. This method of tree planting is still how most trees are planted today, even when many other aspects of forestry work have been mechanised. Weeding followed on to ensure the trees had space to grow; without modern herbicides, this was a manual task using hand sickles.

The availability of sufficient people with forestry knowledge to fulfil the vastly expanding programmes was limited. The first staff were drawn from the former Crown Woods or had come back to the UK with experience from continental Europe and India. They had the important role of imparting their knowledge to the new recruits. From the outset the Forestry Commission began to develop Forestry Training with nine Forestry Training Schools eventually being established across Great Britain from Parkend in the Forest of Dean to Faskally in Scotland. It was in these schools that the foresters needed to carry out the ambitious tree planting programmes were trained, later moving into forest management and timber production. The budget for the first decade of the Forestry Commission included £45,000 to train 45 Forest Officers, 150 Foresters and 600 Foremen. Britain's first degree course in forestry had been created in 1908 at Bangor University, with Edinburgh, Aberdeen and Oxford following in the 1920s after the establishment of the Commission. It was from the pool of graduates from these universities that the first foresters of the organisation were recruited – a mutually beneficial relationship between the universities and the Commission that was to endure. These new courses were most welcome as the Commission needed skilled workers and in 1920 there were reported to be only 41 students attending forester schools. The British forestry industry was starting to expand.

From the outset, ambitious research programmes were established to support the new afforestation venture. The first three Forestry Commission research publications, in 1920, addressed the key challenges of rate of tree and timber growth and understanding forest insect populations – especially pine weevil. In 1926 the Commission carried out a survey of privately owned woodlands, which showed that they were not managed well, and in 1928 the first comprehensive survey of British woodlands as a whole was published. So began a long tradition of survey and research to better understand the forests and to improve techniques and success of management in order to produce high-quality timber.

Planting and establishing the nation's new forests were very labour-intensive and required a huge labour force, much of which was seasonal. As early as 1921, government had identified the afforestation effort as having an important role in the relief of unemployment in rural areas. Forestry was well placed as an industry to do this as its new pockets of land were scattered far and wide, often in sparsely populated rural areas.

So remote were some of the woods that the Commission actually started to form its own communities of dwellings. Planting gangs were recruited from economically depressed industrial areas such as West Cumbria and the North East and labour camps were established in forests such as Thetford. Much of this employment was on a casual basis, often done as 'piecework' – a set fee paid per hundred trees planted, for example.

Such was the progress of the Forestry Commission that by 1929 it managed 242,811 hectares of land across Great Britain with 55,847 hectares planted.

# The 1930s

The financial depression continued into the 1930s and the interwar generation tried to cut its cloth accordingly. Cutbacks were made across government and the Forestry Commission was no exception. However, the Commission was not limited in how it spent the money it possessed and so Commission-owned woodlands continued to be well managed and thrived. Unfortunately, the same could not be said for privately owned woodlands as in this period of financial gloom few landowners were inclined to direct resources towards their woodlands.

Work to establish the nation's timber reserve was steadily being expanded, but it would be fully 20 years or more before any of the growing trees reached an age where timber harvesting could commence with the first thinnings (the periodic removal of a proportion of the trees to provide additional growing space). During the interwar period the Forestry Commission's timber harvest came mainly from the former Crown Woods and from some established woodlands that it had acquired along with land for planting. The standing timber in much of the Crown Woods was of second- or third-class oak, with too many knots or branches and lacking the straightness required for processing into the more valuable wood products. Further deterioration was the result of defoliation by caterpillars and other causes. However, certain of the woods such as Highmeadow, Dymock and Tintern neighbouring the Forest of Dean did contain some excellent young plantations and good timber. The Forestry Commission believed that by studying markets and carefully preparing and classifying produce, timber which was previously unsaleable could now be sold at a profit. By 1934 some of the earliest and fastest-growing plantings were ready for thinning.

The importance placed upon thinning was emphasised by the Chairman of the Forestry Commission Lord Robinson in his note in an inspection report: 'a very good market for small thinnings was developed by Forester Jones, who did excellent pioneer work in timber utilization at Delamere from 1926 to 1939 in obtaining markets for the thinnings'. The main trade developed was for rustic poles, stakes of all sizes down to 1.25 centimetres in diameter, birch brushwood (for horse jumps), firewood and Christmas trees. The rustic poles from the first thinnings of pine plantations were of excellent quality, being very long (up to 7.5 metres) and with very little taper. The market for pine rustic poles had to be created; it was not there waiting for supplies. From 1935 onwards an increasing proportion of the production from thinnings at Delamere was used for pit-props to support the roofs of underground passages in

*Nissen Hut camp in Low Dalby, Dalby Forest, 1934*

the coalmines and peeled timber for the production of wood wool – a shredded timber product used for packaging.

By 1935 a series of 207 sample plots had been established by Forest Research teams covering a variety of tree species, conditions and locations. Regular measurements were taken to establish rate of growth, and to try out different thinning techniques so that their potential could be assessed. These showed Japanese larch to outperform both European larch and Douglas fir, Corsican pine to outperform the native Scots pine, and Sitka spruce to outperform Norway spruce. The programme of sample plots continues to the present day with detailed measurements of tree diameter, height and volume being taken and recorded to form the basis of complex models of tree growth. These models are used to guide planting decisions and provide a sound basis for the calculation of timber volumes and production forecasts. All of this information is published by the Forestry Commission and made available for use by the entire forest industry.

Although in 1935 the Forestry Commission was supplying only 4 per cent by value of the UK timber harvest, it was keen to see a healthy, vibrant timber market into which it could sell its increasing timber production. A study of the home-grown timber market was commissioned which showed that it remained fragmented, ad hoc, and with no system or method. Measures were put in hand to address this and work commenced with the Forest Products Research Laboratory which had the aim of supporting home-grown timber to compete with widely available imports. The first studies looked at the performance of pit-props both in the laboratory and underground, and concluded that home-grown pit-props, properly prepared and graded, were as good as imported ones.

During the 1930s, there was increasing questioning about the impact of the newly created forests on the British landscape and particularly about the use of coniferous rather than broadleaved trees. The newly planted forests could make a harsh impact on the largely treeless landscapes into which they were inserted. Years of sheep grazing had denuded much of upland Britain of its tree cover. Dark green conifers, planted in angular blocks defined by long-established fences and landownership boundaries, could have a significant visual impact, especially in hilly or mountainous terrain. The Forestry Commission had well-rehearsed arguments about the economic and productive performance of conifers and the overwhelming demand for softwood timber (timber from coniferous trees) by industry. However, in response to a strong lobby and petitioning from conservation organisations, such as the Friends of the Lake District, it recognised that it had to relax its single-minded pursuit of rapidly building up the nation's timber reserve and embrace a change of policy to improve amenity and hold back from further afforestation in more sensitive landscapes such as the central Lake District. Elsewhere, the Commission introduced broadleaved belts and groves, gave more careful consideration to the layout of the new forests and their edges, and used a more varied range of species. It also allocated more of the devastated woodlands that had been acquired in Northamptonshire, Hampshire and Sussex for replanting with broadleaved tree species for timber production.

## Access to the Public

The 1930s marked the beginning of a significant new era as recreational access to the forests was established. The Forestry Act of 1927 had recognised the desirability of providing access to woods for the public, and interest in the forests as an escape from the urban environment led to demand for access for recreation. In 1932 hundreds of ramblers attended a Mass Trespass on Kinder Scout in Derbyshire to assert their right to roam, leading to increasing pressure to provide national parks in the UK and to establish formal access rights. The 1931 Committee on National Parks promoted a focus on recreation but at the time lack of publicly owned land was seen as a barrier and there was a reluctance to designate privately owned land that would continue until after the Second World War.

With an increasing portfolio of land, the Forestry Commission was viewed as a potential alternative for recreation and in 1935 the first of the 'National Forest Parks' was created in Argyll; these were renamed 'Forest Parks' after the first National Parks were designated. The newly created recreation site in Argyll contained two campsites and a visitor centre among other attractions. Such was its popularity that the Commission soon planned other parks, one in Snowdonia's Gwydr Forest and the other in the Forest of Dean in Gloucestershire, which was already a popular recreation area. The Forest of Dean park was opened by Colonel Ropner on 12 August 1939: a pavilion of red Canadian cedar was erected in the camping ground, roads and paths were formed by the Forest staff, and the access was enlarged and improved by Gloucestershire County Council. The Forest Parks were sited in larger forests where recreation could be provided on a significant scale; this established recreation as a legitimate activity on the Forestry Commission estate although at the time still subservient to the core purpose of creating forests to produce timber and as a wartime reserve.

# The Second World War 1939–1945

## The Nation's Forests Are Called Upon Again

At the outbreak of war in 1939, 582,747 hectares of land was in management by the Commission with 175,634 hectares planted and 113,312 hectares awaiting planting. However, all the years of planting showed future potential rather than actual timber production. Ninety-six per cent of the UK's timber requirements was supplied by imports, with more than half coming from the Baltic States and Russia, whose vast forests provided large volumes of easily harvested good quality timber through well-established shipping routes to ports on the east coast of Britain. As these supply routes were cut off by war, the need for an assured timber supply became acute and urgent action was required to find alternative sources of timber from within the forests of Britain.

In contrast to the First World War, however, the approach was much more planned. War had been anticipated from the mid-1930s and in 1937 the Forestry Commission and the Board of Trade began planning for a rapid expansion of home timber supply. The aim was for wartime fellings to proceed in an orderly way and, importantly, with reasonable regard to the future of British woodlands. The Forestry Commission undertook a census of woodlands in 1938 using trained, expert staff. Three categories of woodland were identified, with similar quantities of timber available from each: woods which could be felled forthwith; woods which would be felled if necessary; and woods which would be felled only as a matter of extreme urgency.

The Forestry Commission estate was allocated the task of concentrating on the production of pit-props for the mines as these could be most efficiently created from the thinning of younger trees, producing smaller-dimension round timber. The home timber trade was to focus on using larger trees from privately owned woodlands to produce sawn timber for a very wide range of uses including construction, packaging, aircraft, road vehicles and railway wagons, and sleepers for the railways and for coalmine tramroads.

On the day that war was declared, 3 September 1939, the Forestry Commission was divided into two departments. The Forest Management Department proceeded with normal activities, operating a reduced land acquisition and afforestation programme and concentrating on the protection and maintenance of the growing timber resource. The Timber Supply Department was given the priority task of home timber supply until 1941, when this became the responsibility of the Timber Production Department of the Ministry of Supply. Forestry Commission staff formed the backbone of this operation, bringing their experience and ingenuity in timber harvesting to bear on the very many challenges involved in massively accelerating the nation's timber harvest.

Pressure on the Commission to produce timber of all types was intense. The armed forces put in countless special orders for items as diverse as 90-foot (27.4-metre) radio masts and 2.5-foot (0.76-metre) pointed barbed wire entanglement pickets. Early in the war urgent army orders came in for 15-foot (4.6-metre) timber piles to be driven into all the tidal flats and larger flat fields along the coast to prevent the landing of enemy aircraft. As the threat receded, many of these were lifted to be resawn for use in the coalmines. The final stage of the timber harvest in the hardwood forests was to bring in batteries of steel-drum charcoal kilns into which the branch wood was piled for conversion into charcoal for the munitions factories.

Labour was in short supply at the outset of war. The nation's timber production workforce increased from 15,000 at the outbreak to a peak of 73,100 when production was in full swing. The forest industry was then only in the very early and tentative stages of mechanisation. The timber harvest was the product of sheer hard physical labour, working with axes, handsaws and horses. Farm tractors were generally too light to haul timber in the woods, but the ingenuity of the foresters working with local blacksmiths saw all manner of other mechanical aids introduced – aerial ropeways, winches, log chutes and narrow-gauge railways to help move timber. However, at the base of each tree to be felled it was still the physical effort of men and women that drove the timber harvest.

## The Women's Timber Corps (WTC)

Forestry had traditionally been a heavily male-dominated industry, although women had played an important part in forestry during the First World War through the Women's Forestry Service (WFS), formed in 1917 as a subdivision of the Women's Land Army (WLA). The Second World War saw the return of the WFS, renamed the Women's Timber

*Land girls operating a portable Liner saw. Rendlesham Forest, Suffolk, 1945*

Corps (WTC) in 1942, with the women affectionately referred to as 'Lumberjills'. There was an initial reluctance to establish a permanent women's service, due to the danger and physicality of forestry work which was not considered appropriate for them. However, the Forestry Commission undertook a survey of women working in forestry, mainly on private estates, to assess their productivity. The report concluded that women could indeed make an effective contribution, and so the WTC came into being.

The WTC's 6,000 women were an increase over a peacetime workforce of less than 200. Women were attracted to the WTC for a number of reasons: because of family ties with the forest, because their friends had joined, or because they wanted something completely different to their peacetime lives and liked the idea of working outdoors; others thought it was a better option than working in munitions factories.

To begin with, WTC recruitment was through the WLA, of which it was a subdivision. New recruits were aged between 18 and 35, many from diverse employment backgrounds which had no traditional link to the forest industry or the countryside, for whom the prospect of forestry work must have seemed very exciting and exotic. Indeed, the WLA was reluctant to advertise the potential of forestry work to recruits since agricultural work was not considered a prestigious wartime occupation, and it was feared that, if forestry were also offered, it would make land work less attractive. Whereas the WLA struggled to attract new members, the WTC was never short of recruits since it offered travel, better hours and more generous pay.

Before embarking on their new adventure as Lumberjills, the women underwent a month's training in the key skills needed for forestry work. Training camps in England were based in Culford in Suffolk, Hereford in Herefordshire, Wetherby in West Yorkshire, and Lydney in Gloucestershire. These varied, but all were fairly basic and involved communal living with approximately 50 women being trained at any one time. The training itself was not meant to be comprehensive, but rather to instil the basics and a respect for the tools, and to serve as a transition between home and the woods. Learning to use an axe stuck in many of the women's minds, the wielding of a sharp implement being an alien experience. They started off learning how to swing a 4-pound (1.8-kilo) axe, graduating to a 7-pound (3.2-kilo) axe once they had got used to the weight. With most unaccustomed to manual labour, many felt the full impact with aching limbs and sore hands. One Lumberjill, Jessie White, recalls: 'The first lesson to be learnt was how to swing a 4-lb axe, and the next morning the whole hut echoed to moans and groans as we tried to get up from the hard little beds, all limbs aching and sore hands' (BBC 2005, WW2 People's War).

## Vital War Work

The women worked in gangs across England, Scotland and Wales, surveying, clearing and processing standing timber into essential wartime commodities. The life of a Lumberjill was nomadic due to the nature of the work; once one forest had been harvested and cleared, they moved on to the next posting which could be in an entirely different part of the country with new people, working across private and Crown-owned forests. Some of the vital work that the women undertook included creating the tracks that were used during the D-Day landings, producing telegraph poles that maintained essential lines of communication, and producing the charcoal that created the smokescreen under which the Allies were able to cross the Rhine in 1945. They were instrumental in keeping the mining industry going by producing pit-props – a crucial job, as in early 1940 stocks of pit wood were estimated to last for only a maximum of seven months. Other notable contributions included processing the timber that was used to construct the de Havilland Mosquito, one of the fastest operational aircraft at the time.

More trees were needed to meet the increased demand for timber production and from the very early days of the war, women worked in the acquisition of private woodlands. The process of acquisition was based on previous surveys of the country's forests which had been undertaken at the outset of the war in preparation for increasing the timber supply. Anstace Goodhart provides a colourful account of her time working in acquisition in her book *Meet the Members*. After training on the job shadowing existing staff, Anstace travelled extensively, staying only a fortnight or so in any one place, contacting landowners of the trees that had been earmarked for the war effort. Contact was mostly made by knocking on people's doors and explaining that their trees were urgently needed. Sometimes persuasion was needed for the landowner to relinquish their assets and on occasion compromises were necessary, such as agreeing to leave one or two special trees. Once the owner had consented, the women drew up maps showing the extraction routes and stacking grounds, as well as providing calculations of the estimated amount of timber. Anstace met a range of people and travelled widely, finding herself in a number of interesting situations including being threatened by an irate owner with a cut-throat razor, nearly being shot at when working close to a military range, and once being arrested as a suspicious character on the outskirts of an aerodrome. As Anstace said, the work was certainly 'never dull!'

By 1943, the proportion of the nation's total timber supply being produced from home sources had increased from 4 to 65 per cent. In this remarkable achievement, the skilled foresters, sawmillers and estate workers were supported by an influx of additional labour from British Army Forestry Companies, the civilian population, Italian and German

*Planting the early forests. The worker carried the young trees in a bag on their shoulder and planted these individually by hand with a spade or mattock. Most tree planting is still carried out in the same way today*

prisoners of war, and expert help from friendly countries. The Canadian Forestry Corps came fully equipped to operate at scale and worked mainly in the north of Scotland. The Newfoundland Forestry Corps was a voluntary civilian unit recruited by radio appeal which by January 1940 numbered 2,150 men; they worked in 71 separate locations including the New Forest and Yorkshire. Australia and New Zealand sent military engineering units with the New Zealanders operating sawmills in Cirencester in Gloucestershire, Savernake in Wiltshire, and Petersfield in Hampshire. British Honduras (now Belize), at the time the UK's only colony in Central America, also sent a contingent of 539 men by 1941. Unfortunately, one of the boats bringing the men was torpedoed. Thankfully, no lives were lost, but the Hondurans arrived to start their work in a Scottish winter with nothing more than the clothes they stood up in.

Before Canadians started to arrive to help meet wartime demand for timber, work was done by steam-, horse- and manpower. Ian McInnes, a forestry worker in the northern edge of the Cairngorms National Park, describes cutting timber in the 1940s: 'at that time, it was a steam sawmill, but they were portable, the engine was pulled into the middle of the forest. In them days, you took the sawmill to the wood, nowadays you take the wood to the sawmill.' In the Canadian camp, by contrast, they used a diesel-powered sawmill as well as bulldozers and tractors. Many bulldozers were imported from Canada or Newfoundland to work in Strathspey woodlands, and many continued in use after the war. Speaking of the impact of Canadians living in his community as a result of the war, McInnes acknowledges that 'The Canadians revolutionised forestry.'

Canadian forestry used better machinery, but not all of its approaches were an improvement on those in Britain. In North America timber was an apparently limitless resource and there were anecdotes about the sheer amount of timber that North Americans would waste from a tree because they just did not need to harvest it efficiently. While the mantra for a 20th-century British forester was 'an inch off the bottom is worth a foot at the top!', American loggers would 'lay in' (make the first cut) at waist height. Describing felling sites and clearance of materials, one British forester said that 'for some sites, you'd have been able to drive a car right across it, the stumps had been taken so low and even the small brash gathered up to burn and keep the lads warm'. Until very late into the 20th century, foresters in North America often wouldn't replant on any meaningful scale. By contrast, the British productive forests had often been painstakingly hand-planted on land that had either been adapted from another use (often grazing) or that had never been productive (such as deep peat and the upland moors). Other British forests had been closely cultivated from time immemorial, such as the many treasured private estates. British foresters were impressed by the machinery that North American foresters brought to forestry, but they were often appalled by how wastefully inefficient they were with the trees.

The Forestry Commission made a substantial contribution to the war effort, and its value – alongside that of a coherent British forestry policy – was established beyond doubt. Its staff had formed the backbone of the wartime timber effort. Despite the immaturity of its new timber reserve, using careful assessment of the older Crown Woods and other acquired forests, the Forestry Commission sold to the Board of Trade Timber Production Department for purposes directly connected to the war effort a total of 51,250,000 cubic feet (1,450,000 cubic metres) of timber - enough to fill 580 Olympic swimming pools. This comprised 34,750,000 cubic feet (980,000 cubic metres) of conifers and 16,500,000 cubic feet (470,000 cubic metres) of broadleaves with a value of £2,231,000. This timber filled a great variety of needs from poles for military defences, to veneer logs, to sawn timber of all grades, to mining timber, right down to pea sticks and beanpoles from the underwood needed to support the 'Dig for Victory' efforts of farmers and gardeners.

The Forestry Commission was not always ready to give up its most magnificent trees, even in wartime, unless there was an absolute need. On one occasion the authorities requested the supply of poles from 36 trees in some of the nation's most magnificent stands of European larch at Tintern in the Wye Valley and at Highmeadow in the Forest of Dean, each pole to be at least 90 feet (27 metres) long and 14 square inches (90 square centimetres) at the base. These were to be stored at Gloucester Bridge over the River Severn so that, should enemy bombing destroy the bridge, a temporary crossing could speedily be constructed on this vital route into South Wales. The trees were duly marked for felling, but in a last-minute compromise it was agreed to keep them standing after the Commission guaranteed that they would be felled and transported to Gloucester within 24 hours on receipt of an SOS call (which happily never came).

At the end of the war, the timber resource that had been created with so much concentrated effort since 1919 remained largely in good shape. The outstanding work of the Forestry Commission's Forest Management Department, operating largely in the shadow of its timber-producing sister department, had ensured that, working within the limits of the availability of labour and finance, the developing forest was protected and maintained and the vital thinning programmes achieved. The amount of direct damage to State forests by the waging of war was remarkably small: 809 hectares had been destroyed by enemy action, 830 hectares destroyed by military training (principally by fire), and 688 hectares lost to construction of camps, depots and aerodromes. The expansion of the timber resource had slowed, but still an additional 40,469 hectares had been planted and 53,823 hectares of plantable land acquired. There was much work to be done in the post-war period, but the basis of a timber reserve remained intact and the Forestry Commission and its staff stood ready to play their part in meeting the challenge of renewal and reconstruction.

# The Post-War Period, 1945–1949

After six years of heroic effort to ensure that the country did not run short of timber, awareness of the need to grow trees had once again been raised. On 1 June 1945, shortly before the general election that brought Attlee's Labour government to power, Churchill's wartime government quickly passed the Forestry Act. This brought the Forestry Commission jointly under the control of the Ministry of Agriculture and Fisheries and the Secretary of State for Scotland, transferring actual ownership of the land to the appropriate ministers. Although this took away some of the authority of the Commissioners, who had previously been able to act independently, it also highlighted the increasingly prominent and important status given to forestry in Britain.

A change of government did not reduce the enthusiasm for forestry; indeed, it could even be said to have increased it. The incoming Minister of Agriculture and Fisheries, Tom Williams, could hardly have been more supportive, proposing the replenishment of the Forestry Fund by £20 million. This was intended to finance afforestation and the replanting of 147,710 hectares from 1946 to 1950 – an incredibly ambitious target of 117,359 hectares in the State forests and 30,351 hectares in the private sector, and the maximum the Commissioners had recommended.

The focus on private forests, albeit at a low level, was long overdue as the post-war assessment of the area, volume and growth rate of the forests of Britain demonstrated. From 1947 to 1949 this assessment was undertaken by the census team, led by Jack Chard. A prominent staff member in the Forestry Commission, Chard had also been involved in the 1938 census of timber in Britain which had been aborted as a result of the war. During the war he was involved in the timber production effort and took the rather novel approach of employing out-of-work circus elephants to help move the logs! His team, which included two of the first female District Officers, assessed every parcel of woodland in Britain of more than 2 hectares. As well as land managed by the Commission, they also assessed woodland held by private landowners and local authorities. The team carefully mapped and recorded the results on punched cards. Seen through a modern lens it is unfortunate that the records do not cover biodiversity, but inevitably with the fog of war still lying heavy, the team focused on the ability of the forests to produce timber. The picture in private woodlands was not a happy one: of the 1,143,371 hectares in private hands (82 per cent of the country's total woodland coverage), only 865,539 were supporting a worthwhile crop. The land displayed an average growth rate of about 2 cubic metres per hectare per annum, about one-third of what was felt to be a reasonable rate of production. The remaining 277,832 hectares were seen as derelict, waste or nearly waste land. A modern view might see 75 per cent of the forest being productive as a good balance between timber production and conservation. Priorities post-war were very different.

The disclosures of the census should not have come as a surprise to foresters. The results reflected more than a century of a limited economic rationale for the management of forests. Further, the high timber demands of the war had caused the felling of virtually all the best managed stands. The tragedy of the forced fellings of the world wars still haunts forestry in Britain today. Little survived those years: in the main only the oldest broadleaf woods, which were seen as 'over mature' for sawmilling in 1939, poor-quality unmanaged coppice and younger conifer plantations, which were mostly Forestry Commission woodland not yet ready for felling. This compounded the deforestation and neglect of the 19th century to leave British forests and forestry in a sorry state. The diminished state of hardwood forestry in particular, in sharp contrast to parts of the European continent, lingers on as an enduring weakness in British forestry to this day. During the war some 1,200 million cubic feet of standing timber were felled and milled. By 1947 only 2,658 million cubic feet remained as standing timber. In the six years of the war the country had consumed around one-third of its home-grown timber resources, including most of the best woods, so while the forests themselves had not been damaged by bombing, the impact of this period on the forests was significant.

Although the Forestry Commission had subsidised private woodland since its very early days, the reality was that such support was of limited

*The Soldtrac plough – one of the lightest ploughs used in moorland afforestation. Pulled by a D2 tractor. It cuts a furrow 10–14" deep, turning out a satisfactory turf for planting. Kielder, 1949*

value and impact until after the Second World War. Initially in 1919, support was offered by loans charging 4-per-cent interest, which were unsurprisingly ignored, and it was only in 1921 that non-repayable grants began to be offered as schemes to alleviate high levels of unemployment. These grants ceased in 1926 and were replaced by a less generous scheme offering £2 per acre (0.4 hectare) for conifers and £4 per acre for broadleaves, equivalent to one-fifth or one-third of average planting costs, and were only sufficient to encourage planting rates of about 2,000 hectares per annum during the 1930s. This rate of planting was felt to be inadequate and one of the proposals of the Commissioners' 1943 Post-War Forest Policy paper was a scheme of 'dedication' in which private woodland owners committed themselves to practise forestry and produce timber in perpetuity in exchange for higher levels of State support. The idea was discussed widely with the various forestry societies from both England and Scotland and associations such as the Country Landowners' Association, with many landowners concerned that it might amount to back-door nationalisation. On 1 November 1945 the Dedication Scheme (Basis I and Basis II) was approved by the government. Basis I, subject to certain conditions to ensure a reasonable level of silviculture, provided support of 25 per cent of the costs of managing woods until they reached profitability. Basis II was a planting grant on areas with

*Planning the census, 1950*

an approved plan, which paid a maintenance grant for 15 years. The Dedication Scheme was officially launched in 1947. This was a radical statement of support, even if one that was initially slow to be taken up, and demonstrated the national importance of the timber industry. The role of the Forestry Commission in directing this was carried out on the ground by the Woodland Officers. Their role in advising landowners not just on the technical aspects of forestry but also on the legal aspects and the availability of government funding to support privately owned forests for the benefits of the nation was one that would grow and grow.

The planting target for State forests from 1946 to 1950 had been set by the Minister of Agriculture and Fisheries Tom Williams at 117,359 hectares – an ambitious one. By 1950 a creditable 88,038 hectares of new State forest had been planted. The Commission had fallen short, not through lack of money or ambition, but rather due to difficulties in finding land.

The main problem faced by the Commission in the acquisition of land following the Second World War was that land was also in high demand for agricultural purposes. Just as the government was encouraging an expansion of forestry in Britain, so it was also offering financial incentives to increase food production. The challenges of these and other competing demands on land use would only grow in later years. Prior to the war, government had seemed content to import cheap food from the Empire, rather than prioritise growing it internally, and as a result there had been a climate of wholesale land transfer at low values, which had aided the ambitions of the Commission. In contrast, after the war the Ministry of Agriculture and Fisheries changed its policy and became keen to encourage self-sufficiency and the preservation of productive agricultural land. Landowners were naturally reluctant to sell a productive asset and in some cases were taking land out of forestry to put it to use in farming.

## Rebuilding and Expanding the Timber Reserve and Increasing Timber Production

Planting, which had initially been held back in the immediate aftermath of the war due to shortages of machinery used to support the war effort, soon resumed apace towards the end of the decade. and during the 1950s included substantial areas of broadleaved trees in the south of England – oak and particularly beech on the downlands.

The two post-war timber production priorities for the Forestry Commission were the expansion of thinnings from the rapidly developing forests planted during the 1920s and 1930s, and tackling the management of the low-grade hardwood timber characteristic of many of the lowland woodlands and former coppices in the south of England. The twin challenges it faced were expanding and developing the resources needed to undertake the timber harvest and ensuring the availability of markets for the timber that was produced.

The timber harvest continued to be dominated by physical manpower. The cross-cut saw and axe were used for felling, debranching and cross-cutting (dividing the tree into lengths for various products), and horses extracted the timber from the felling site to the roadside. The use of tractors was in its early infancy and the chainsaw had yet to make an impact. As the Forestry Commission's newly established forests came into production, large numbers of workers were required in remote rural areas. Output per worker was very modest using manual methods and it was envisaged that forest communities such as Kielder Village would need to expand substantially to house the tens of thousands of workers who would eventually be required for the timber harvest when the forests were in full production. A major house-building programme was launched to create forest villages to supplement the existing network of forest workers' holdings.

## Homes and Communities

Since its earliest days, the Forestry Commission had recognised the need to retain populations in rural areas, particularly in remote places such as the Highlands, as its annual report of 1924 makes clear:

It will be observed that the forest workers' holding is not intended to provide full-time work for the occupier, but to serve the double end of identifying him with the progress of the forest and affording an industrious man opportunities of improving his standard of living.

There were 624 holdings recorded for Great Britain in 1924. They consisted of a cottage and garden 'with enclosed agricultural or cultivable land and a maximum of 10 acres (4 hectares), enough to allow the occupant to keep a couple of cows, and to grow potatoes and other crops'. Although this may have been the original intention, a holding of 10 acres (4 hectares) was rare, most being between 1 and 5 acres (0.4 and 2 hectares). There were usually two types, some being 'proper' holdings and others being long and narrow, often known as 'chicken runs'. In Kielder Village, for example, there were around 56 holdings, consisting of cottages with about a quarter-acre (0.1 hectare) of 'garden' each to grow vegetables and an additional acre of land with buildings on for keeping livestock such as pigs and chickens. Forest workers were allowed unpaid time off to work their land, particularly at key times such as harvest, but although this supplemented forestry work, it was impossible to grow enough to live off.

Voices of the Forest, a collection of interviews with people working in Thetford Forest in Norfolk, describes a design

> similar in almost every way to the highland croft – no doubt the inspiration – except that the occupant was guaranteed by the Commission 'not less than 150 days' work in the forest, for the most part at piece work rates'. This would boost wages above those of agricultural workers. These holdings would be let on 364-day tenancies, so that they would remain Commission property – tied cottages in effect with no security of tenure unlike traditional crofts – and their total number was to be limited so that there would be no more than five for every 1,000 acres [405 hectares] of forest land acquired.

Forest holdings were for married men and their families. Single men, both workers and foresters, were all housed in other premises, such as hostels, sometimes for many years. In Scotland these were known as 'bothies'. The quality of accommodation varied considerably, and because many of them were ex-army buildings from the war their condition would often deteriorate over time. Other bothies could be cottages or farmhouses, sometimes referred to as tea houses. John Keenleyside, a young Assistant Forester at the time, recalls staying at the Dublin Bothy in Ross-shire. The wooden hut contained dormitory-style accommodation for 32 men on ex-army beds, a dining room and a kitchen, with a corrugated iron lean-to outside that served as the 'ablution block'. Although the accommodation was basic, there was 'an element of camaraderie' among the workers.

In the interwar years, holdings were seen as costly to maintain. Sir John Stirling Maxwell, third Chair of the Commission, writing in the 1930s, lamented that 'the planting of forest workers on the land is a more anxious and much more expensive business than the planting of trees'. With the scaling-up of State forestry after the Second World War, investment in forest villages really took off, the scale of investment differing according to the landscape and the level of manpower required.

Forestry in Britain changed a great deal in the immediate post-war period, not least in staff numbers. As the Commission's workload had grown, so too had its ranks, and although 1,400 dwellings were already owned for the purposes of forester homes, by 1949 the Commission was employing around 13,200 people and it was clear many more were required. Work began in 1949 on creating forest villages, and in 1950 eight new villages started to be built in the Borders alone. These villages were for the use of foresters and their families, and were carefully located to facilitate work in often remote rural areas where housing had not previously existed. The first new residents of the forest village of Ae in Scotland moved into their homes in 1949, with the very first birth in the village occurring the following January. The creation of new housing, aiding as it did the ability to work in the countryside, was also welcomed in many quarters as it appeared to counter the growing trend for young people to move to urban areas. In some areas the Commission bought or built housing in existing villages, but other areas being worked were so out of the way that entire hamlets and villages ended up being produced and owned by the organisation.

One forester describes the need for the villages:

People were moving to areas for work where there was no housing, so we built forest villages to house them so that we could actually get the forests planted and managed. This was not just to do with protection of the forest but was really absolutely essential to being able to manage them. It's difficult to comprehend from the modern age just how poor communications were back then, especially in these remote locations.

Forest workers had to be close to the forest at all times, not just to offer them the benefit of a short commute, but also so they could stay constantly vigilant for forest fire – this was true even in the 1980s, long after the heyday of the workers' holdings.

The Commission tried to support the communities it either came to dominate or had created. In Ae, where the Commission built 50 homes – the last completed in 1967 – conditions were at first basic, with electricity only installed in 1950. In 1952 the Commission donated an old army hut to use as a 'temporary' village hall – this remained in use until it was declared unsafe in 1993 and demolished in 1997. Facilities gradually improved with a shop and post office opened in 1956 and a school in 1958. The Commission helped the new communities by providing fuel logs for pensioners and workers, supporting children's parties, endorsing the use of official vehicles to give lifts into town in places with no public transport and, in the era before affordable private transport, allowing time off work during family crisis, providing private health-care (at times), and giving work to local people with disabilities. In the rural Northumberland village of Falstone, the Commission provided a private healthcare system for 'a few coppers a week' to workers and their families, which was extremely helpful in the remote location where they were placed. Although it didn't cover major operations it included free doctor visits and free prescriptions.

With very tough working and environmental conditions, no entertainment and few local amenities, forestry villages in remote locations developed a very strong sense of community. There were thriving youth clubs, churches and sports teams – in one Forestry Commission district there were even enough teams for a football league! People were born in the villages and lived their whole lives there in communities utterly dominated by forestry – just as in pit villages, where every person lived their lives to the routine of the pit. Earning a wage from the Commission and doing well within the community was the culture, a 'culture of work', defined by a single large employer and played out in thousands of people's lives. The communities created around the work of the foresters were a huge part of the story of the Forestry Commission, and central to the lives of generations of workers and their families.

## An Expanding Timber Market

After the war the Forestry Commission also began to increase the proportion of its timber sold 'standing' to timber merchants. These merchants brought their own timber cutters into the forests to harvest the timber which they then sold on to timber users. This was a way of increasing the timber harvesting resource and also of reducing costs, particularly where harvesting programmes were too small or variable for efficient use of its own manpower and machinery.

Much of the increasing harvest of timber was conifer roundwood, (short logs of small diameter), and the main markets continued to be in fencing, rustic poles and pit-props. However, the development of new high-volume markets was required to ensure the success of the rapidly expanding thinning programme which was necessary if the very best trees in the forest were to have the space to grow into the high-quality large-dimension timber that would provide the foundation for a new sawmilling industry to develop.

While harvesting from the Forestry Commission's new conifer forests developed apace, market opportunities for low-grade hardwood timber became increasingly difficult to find, especially as the nationalised mines turned increasingly to the use of conifer timber, and steel replaced wood in the manufacture of railway wagon bodies. Lower grade timber is characterised by a lack of straightness, the presence of knots and branches, and in oak by 'shake' where cracks run up through the wood so that it falls apart when sawn. The development of a new hardwood pulping mill at Sudbrook in Monmouthshire in the late 1950s brought much-needed capacity and was supported by long-term timber-supply guarantees from the Forestry Commission. Most timber was previously sold on short-term contracts of three to 12 months by tender or auction, but longer-term contracts were beginning to be offered as the Commission developed its role in supporting large-scale industrial development in timber processing for the benefit of the whole British forestry sector.

Timber harvesting requires the provision of good-quality all-weather roads within the forest so that lorries can safely haul wood products to the processing plants. On Forestry Commission land it was the Commission's responsibility to plan, construct and maintain these vital forest roads. The earliest programme of road building came after the First World War in the Crown Woods and was primarily for the relief of unemployment. This was followed in the 1930s by the expansion of the Ministry of Labour's rehabilitation camps. As the objective was to maximise outdoor employment, most of the work was done by hand with excellent results, but at about one-tenth the efficiency that could have been achieved with the machinery of the time.

The fast-expanding road programme urgently needed to enable thinning operations had been interrupted by the Second World War. In 1946 the government approved the Forest Roads Scheme with the twin objectives of facilitating extraction of forest produce and making a contribution to the relief of unemployment, including that of the Polish Resettlement Corps. The programme's objective was to use as many men and as little machinery as possible and by 1947 3,452 men were employed with a focus on those parts of the country where unemployment was highest, rather than where roads were most needed. Fortunately, with a decline in unemployment, road building activity was able to move to a more planned basis, finding the most efficient methods of construction and specifications that would work across the great variety of terrain where roads were needed.

The initial road specification was to excavate down to a solid base, lay a bottom foundation of large hardcore, spread smaller metalling, and then roll to form a surface with a camber to allow the shedding of rainfall. Maintaining gentle curves and a gradient of no more than 1:10 is important to keep vehicles moving and avoid erosion. The specification had to be adapted on wet ground by first creating drains 5 metres or so away from the road alignment to keep the road line as dry as possible and then to lay the road material onto growing heather, supplemented by woody material where available, to form a raft supporting the road formation. Tremendous lengths of road were also built across far more difficult rocky and mountainous country involving heavy excavations, blasting, construction of bridges, and moving of rock and soil. Regular maintenance to shape and compact the running surface was undertaken by a motor grader and vibrating roller.

Along with the roads came the construction of bridges – often made from Forestry Commission timber – the opening of quarries to provide roadstone, and the creation of hard standings for handling and loading of timber. Forest Engineering was set up from scratch in 1946 with the twin roles of building forest roads, and developing and maintaining machinery. Some of these early engineers found some very innovative solutions to the task at hand, such as Packwood's tramline bridges. As buses were becoming the favoured form of public transport in many towns and cities, tramlines were being lifted across the country. Colonel H. Packwood, who had been in charge of road building in Scotland, noticed that if these were laid side by side and filled with concrete, they created an incredibly strong bridge sufficient for spans of up to 20 feet. Although his approach was rather unorthodox, where these bridges have been maintained, they are still strong enough to be used by modern vehicles. It is to the credit of those involved in the early years that the road network has stood the test of time.

The length of roads needed has decreased as timber extraction has been mechanised. With horses, which were used to extract timber until the 1960s, the maximum economic extraction distance was about 137 metres, so a lorry road spacing of 274 metres or about 5 kilometres of road

*Steam sterilisation of ground by Hoddesdon pipes on the open ground for conifer seedlings. The boiler is on a transporter – the 2-inch steam pipe conveys the steam to a manifold supply of five perforated pipes by flexible hose. Tulliallan Nursery, Kincardine, Fife*

ONE HUNDRED YEARS OF THE FORESTRY COMMISSION

per square kilometre of forests was needed, but these days with modern forwarders extraction distances can be greater and around 1.5 kilometres of road per square kilometre will suffice. At the same time, the roads and bridges have been upgraded to accommodate timber lorries of up to 44 tonnes. The Forestry Commission maintains a network of around 1,000 kilometres of principal forest roads in England for timber haulage. Nowadays, forest roads provide extensive opportunities for recreational access by walkers, cyclists and horse riders and the Civil Engineers' skills are also employed to construct car parks, footpaths and mountain bike trails.

## Staff Culture

The end of the war meant the end of military service for many. Upon their return home the demobbed soldiers needed to find work and one of the many schemes set up to help them train in a new profession was the Forest Workers Training Scheme. Launched in 1946, this one-year course provided practical experience under real working conditions. Forestry Commission woods such as Thetford Forest were used for this purpose. By 1948, 161 new trainee foresters had graduated from British forestry schools including those at Lynford in England, Gwydr in Wales, and Glentress in Scotland.

With the major surges of activity coming after two world wars and with forestry providing employment for many returning military personnel, it is unsurprising that the management structure of the Forestry Commission closely mirrored that of the military, with a hierarchy of Forest or District Officers (Officers), Foresters (NCOs) and Forest Workers. This provided an important dimension of the culture right through to the 1980s and 1990s, only being completely set aside with staff unification in 2000 (see p. 85). The Forestry Commission also provided work for many people who became unemployed as heavy industry suffered the consequences of economic depression and this brought another dimension to the culture with a hard-working approach coupled with robust industrial relations, especially around piecework.

As physical effort was replaced by machine power, new skills and ways of working had to be learned. To those who know the quality and dedication of the Forestry Commission's staff, it comes as no surprise to learn that some of the top harvesting machine operators started their long working lives felling trees with an axe and bow-saw for horses to extract. Very many people have spent their whole working lives with the Forestry Commission and it has not been unusual to see Forest Craftsmen or Wildlife Rangers retire with 50 years of service. While this is often in a single location, many Foresters, Civil Engineers and workers in other disciplines have spent long careers moving around the country, building their experience and knowledge, and making a lifetime commitment to the nation's public forests.

Nowadays, the Forestry Commission's work has become much more diverse and requires a much wider range of skills. Most of the high-volume work of timber harvesting and tree establishment is undertaken by contractors and timber harvesting is now heavily mechanised. Although overall staff numbers are much smaller than in the early decades, and it is more likely that you will meet community recreation rangers than chainsaw operators, the same culture that has prevailed down the years shines through and there is a real devotion to and pride in the forests.

# The 1950s

The Forestry Commission came into being to be responsible for forestry cover and timber reserves for the whole country, not simply those forests and trees owned or directly managed by the Commission itself. The 1951 Forestry Act provided a pivotal moment in the history of the Commission and its role in relation to privately owned woodlands. The Act banned the cutting down of trees without a licence, giving new responsibilities to the Commission, who became responsible for monitoring felling. The motivation behind this move was to maintain the timber reserve of the country as a whole, not least should it be required in a time of war, and reflected the Commission's growing relationship with the private landowner. Although the objectives may have changed, the felling licence regulation – with various caveats and conditions – is still in force today and is handled by Forest Services which sits within the Commission.

The 1950s was a period of huge growth for the Commission. The value of timber sales rose from less than £500,000 per year in 1950 to well over £2 million per year by 1960. The harvesting and marketing of timber had become an important part of the Forestry Commission's work. It was both leading the rapid development of the home-grown timber harvesting and processing industry and generating significant income that, as a public body, would all be ploughed back into the management and development of its forests. Towards the end of the 1950s, a ten-year planting scheme was launched, with particular attention given to Scotland and Wales, and staff being posted to often remote locations in order to provide labour for the planting. Much of the work carried out on Forestry Commission land was still done by hand, and many of the machines still used parts adapted from decommissioned army vehicles. As the 1950s progressed, the Forestry Commission became increasingly concerned to improve efficiency and thus reduce the costs of its rapidly expanding programmes of forest operations.

The Work Study Branch was established in 1956 with four staff and the task of improving efficiency across the whole timber industry by both 'method study' and 'time study'. Its staff made a huge contribution to the development of methods of timber harvesting in the UK, scouring the world for new techniques and equipment or designing it themselves if nothing suitable could be found. Full testing of all these innovations was undertaken and details of those that proved worthy of introduction were published and taken forward in the Forestry Commission's operations in conjunction with training teams. 'Time study' was employed to create standard timetables for a wide range of forestry tasks under different conditions as an aid to setting piecework rates. The Work Study Forester would go out with timber felling or extraction teams and observe their work, stopwatch and clipboard in hand, recording every element of activity. This was not always popular with the Forest Workers, or with the Work Study Foresters themselves. Most work was undertaken on piecework, with the aim of boosting productivity and allowing operators the chance to boost their earnings by around 30 per cent. The timetables greatly aided the setting of rates, in a way that could be understood by both Foresters and Forest Workers. Looking back, there are mixed views about piecework. Some say that it was a good thing: you were paid for the work that you had done and it gave a real incentive to work hard and look after your equipment. Others say that the pressure of piecework led to cutting corners and, indeed, it was not applied to more hazardous tasks such as clearing wind-blown trees. The Kielder chainsaw operators remember that:

> On every new site there was always an argument when the piecework rate was set. If they had made good money on the last site, then the Forester would cut the rate for the next one. Sometimes there were 'dust ups' over 0.1 of a penny per tree and the operators would move to a 'go slow' if a rate couldn't be agreed. The biggest problem was that one operator would always think that somebody else had a better rate or easier trees in their part of the crop.

## Multipurpose Forestry

The concept of multipurpose forestry, recognising the importance of wildlife and people in forestry management, was first explored in the late 1950s and 1960s, though it would take several decades before this became integral to the Commission's work. Jack Chard, the Forestry Commission's Conservator for North West England, and Bill Grant, Chief Forester at Grizedale, saw the opportunity for a truly integrated approach to forest management that would recognise wildlife conservation and management, alongside opportunities for public access and recreation, as valid objectives to be pursued in conjunction with timber production. Inspired by the United States, where the multiple uses and value of forests had been brought into the public consciousness and where forest rangers had become almost legendary figures in the eyes of young Americans, this was the initial foray into the multipurpose management of its land that sits at the heart of the Forestry Commission's activities today.

Jack Chard's experimentation with wildlife management began at Grizedale Forest in the southern Lake District. As a response to criticism of the Forestry Commission's approach to deer management (see 'The Beginnings of Conservation', p. 59), he proposed the development of a 'humane approach to the control and management of deer', recruiting the first Game Warden – the charismatic Herbert Fooks – in 1956. By the time Fooks left four years later he had put deer control onto a humane and scientific footing, trained Rangers in the job, and started a small Deer Museum. This approach began to be rolled out more generally across the Forestry Commission and the first Wildlife Ranger was appointed in 1964, responsible for ensuring the delicate balance between animals and forestry within the forests. Today it would be inconceivable to take a forest under management without ensuring it had a Wildlife Ranger assigned to cover it.

A new and unforeseen development was the increasing use of Commission woods as filming locations. As the film industry started to shoot more scenes on location, Commission woods started to be used and in the 1950s they secured their first big name as the 1953 film *Rob Roy* included various scenes shot in Loch Ard Forest in Scotland. The famous shoot involved building not only period cottages but also a fort, and a complex battle scene was shot on Corriegrennan Hill. Filming in Commission woods continues to be popular and over the years a large number of famous films, adverts and television scenes have been shot among the trees. Today, Bourne Wood in Hampshire is the location most often used by production companies, its credits including the opening scenes of *Gladiator*.

# The 1960s

The 1960s was a time of great change and excitement within the Forestry Commission, culminating in the celebrations of its 50th anniversary in 1969. The literal fruits of its labour, in the form of larger dimension timber, started to be harvested and for the first time the Commission took its place as a significant vendor of timber. The decade also saw an increasing emphasis on mechanisation. At the same time, the maturing organisation found itself ready to expand its gaze and incorporate new considerations such as landscape architecture and wildlife.

Since its foundation in 1919, it had been anticipated that the day would come when the trees the Commission had planted could start to be sold in large quantities, and this began in the 1960s. Previously, timber produced by the Commission had been either the product of trees planted prior to 1919 or the result of thinning trees planted by the Commission. Today, Forestry England, Forestry and Land Scotland, and Natural Resources Wales are together the largest producer of timber in Britain.

*Head Keeper Bert Smith, along with his dog, communicating by radio.*
*New Forest, Hampshire, 1966*

The decade saw many new developments within the organisation. In 1965 the first full-time Commissioners were appointed and given executive responsibility for administration and finance, forest and estate management, and harvesting and marketing. Senior Officer posts were introduced in Scotland and Wales to deal with the special implications of policy and operations in these countries.

The 1960s also saw significant changes in the education and training of foresters. With the closure of its internal forestry schools, the Commission looked to the public education system to provide forester courses. In 1969 a Diploma in Forestry was established at Cumberland and Westmorland College of Agriculture and Forestry at Newton Rigg and became one of the main catalysts in changing the military-style hierarchy that then existed and in eventually breaking down the barrier between the different classes of worker, forester and forest officer. One student remarked: 'Newton Rigg didn't feel hierarchical, and when you came into the Forestry Commission you could tell that this was a big departure from the way things had been done. Just the expectations of people coming out didn't have that same kind of rigid acceptance of hierarchy.'

## The Beginnings of Conservation

Some of the mid-century attitudes to the treatment of wildlife are described by Ian Fraser who was then in his early career as a trapper at Glenmore:

> In those years, forestry gamekeepers shot everything all year round. They just slaughtered everything. We used to get paid sixpence for shooting a red squirrel, ten shillings for shooting a fox, ... I shot maybe ten or twelve capers [capercaillie] in a week.

Anyone familiar with the conservation status of British wildlife will know how rare and endangered many of those species now are.

Attitudes began to change in the 1960s. Before the Deer Act of 1963 many different means were used to kill deer. They were considered vermin to be got rid of, and were killed with snares, shotguns or whatever was effective. The Deer Act changed all that by bringing in rules on when and where deer could be managed. When killing deer a high-powered rifle had to be used, and it became illegal to take females when they could have dependent young that might starve. As a government department, the Forestry Commission embraced this change quickly, and the welfare of the animal became a central part of policy.

There were experiments in reintroduction of native wildlife as part of the new approach at Grizedale – greylag geese and polecats were successful, though unsurprisingly plans to reintroduce bison were never realised! This bold tradition lives on today – subject of course to much more stringent licensing and monitoring – with the Forestry Commission's ongoing programmes to reintroduce major species including pine marten, beaver and white-tailed sea eagles.

Steps were made to improve the experience of visitors coming to the forests to get closer to nature, notably at Grizedale where the first nature trail was established in 1961 and a campsite quickly followed to enable people to stay overnight in the forest environment. A network of tarns was established, using a combination of low-cost turf dams and blasting with explosives to create deeper water. The first wildlife-viewing hide 'Tree Tops' was constructed in 1964 and more smaller hides followed.

Forest Planning and Landscape Design

While there were some good examples of sensitivity to landscape and people in the planting of the early forests, particularly in the National Parks, the motivation was primarily about planting trees and establishing the nation's timber reserve. As the forests began to reach maturity in the 1960s, much the same approach was initially applied. The forests had been laid out in grid patterns and the early felling was often a 'rolling up the carpet' of the first-rotation forests and putting similar forests in their place.

The immediate practical problem was with wind-blow. A forest edge that has been exposed to the prevailing wind throughout its life will develop a strong measure of resistance to its effect. However, as soon as felling begins, a new forest edge is created where the trees have spent their whole life sheltered by other trees and have little resistance even to modest winds. The effects can be devastating, and although wind-blown trees can be harvested and used, the work is more costly and hazardous and there is significant wastage. Public response to unsightly extensive timber harvesting also became an issue and with this came a realisation that the harvesting of the first rotation provided a 'once in 50 years' opportunity to create something different. The 'plantations' of closely planted trees, established in a grid pattern and covering as much of the available land area as possible in order to build the timber reserve, could – with careful thought and planning – be transformed into 'forests for the future' to serve the wider needs of amenity, recreation and wildlife at the same time as reducing the impact of wind-blow by creating more open space and wind-firm edges. This approach also tied in with the new directions from government which in 1963, while reaffirming the importance of timber production, committed the Forestry Commission to bear in mind the need, wherever possible, 'to provide public access and recreation, and devote more attention to increasing the beauty of the landscape'. This broader commitment grew ever stronger over subsequent decades of forest policy.

At first, special attention was given to sensitive landscapes. The first landscape architects were employed, adding a new discipline to those already involved in planning and implementing the Forestry Commission's timber production activity. In 1963 the renowned landscape architect Sylvia Crowe was engaged to provide advice and went on to work for the Commission for 13 years. Landscape Plans were devised under Crowe's direction for places such as the Ennerdale Valley and Dodd Wood in the Lake District. The form of the landscape was analysed and this guided the design of the shape of the felling areas and the shapes and species to be used in replanting. The forest foreman responsible for marking out the felling areas at Dodd Wood observed:

> Before Dame Sylvia's landscape plan, it was easy to mark out the felling areas – everything was square and followed straight lines – but then there were all sorts of fancy shapes to mark out and the boundaries went through different crops. It was much more complicated, but everything was visible on the side of the hill and now the shapes are established it all looks much better.

## The Forests Reach Maturity

The 1960s were years of consolidation and confident expansion as the early plantings reached maturity and were ready for felling and replanting. Not only was the overall volume of timber increasing rapidly, but as the trees continued to grow, the average size of the trees being harvested increased too. This meant that much more of the timber was suitable for new and higher value uses. The logs produced were now large enough for the sawmills to convert them efficiently into sawn timber products for the construction, fencing and packaging industries.

The Forestry Commission compiled and published annual long-term production forecasts, which set out how much timber would be produced from its forests over a period of 20 years. In conjunction with regular timber sales and timber supply guarantees, this gave timber-processing companies the confidence to expand and invest in new facilities, which included major pulp, paper and particle-board plants in locations such as Workington, Hexham and Ellesmere Port. These new plants were

*Demonstration of extraction of thinnings by Isachsen double-drum winch to Bedford articulated lorry with Hiab hoist. Durris Forest, Grampian, 1963*

strategically located in relation to the expanding timber supply from Kielder, the Lake District, Wales and South Scotland and were able to replace imports in supplying their products to domestic markets.

It was the combination of the timber rapidly coming on stream from its new forests and the provision of good information about the timber resource, along with the Forestry Commission's role in promoting and supporting the growth of timber processing, that set the climate for change. The rapid development of a modern British timber-processing industry with the associated new jobs and economic growth represented a significant return on the investment decisions that had been made by government through the first half of the 20th century. These decisions, together with the hard work of the Commission's staff and contractors, provided the foundation of the continued growth and development which took place over the following 50 years.

The period after 1960 saw rapid changes in the way that timber was harvested and transported. The increasing availability of new equipment and machinery, and the drive to find more efficient working techniques, meant that conventional thinking on how timber would be harvested which had guided the planning and development of the forests – and particularly their manpower requirements – was set to change beyond recognition.

## Early Mechanisation

Until 1960, tree felling was undertaken almost entirely by manual methods. The everyday tools that had been in use for decades were the cross-cut saw and the axe, with the bow-saw also employed for the smallest trees in first thinnings. The work was physically demanding and highly skilled. Experienced tree fellers knew just how much effort to employ and the pulling cut with the saw was made using their whole body, rather than just their arms. It might not have been called 'ergonomics' in those days, but the tree fellers knew how to do their work efficiently, making best use of their bodily strength.

The first chainsaws had begun to appear in the 1950s but they were generally heavy and cumbersome. Weighing more than 20 kilos, they required two people to operate them and were not well suited to forest terrain. However, as saws became lighter and more manoeuvrable and suited to one-man operation, they rapidly began to be adopted. A revolution in tree felling had begun. A large tree that might take an hour for two men to fell using axe and cross-cut saw could be felled in five minutes by one man with a chainsaw. Between 1960 and 1969 the number of chainsaws in use quadrupled; they became lighter, smaller and more versatile; and one-operator working became the norm with an annual output of around 700 cubic metres per saw.

Once the tree was on the ground, the branches had to be removed. This was where the axe came into its own, with the tree fellers moving along the stem, removing the branches as they went. At first, the early chainsaws were not light or agile enough to replace the axe for de-limbing (also known as 'snedding'), but as they improved and new models were imported from Scandinavia, they took on both the felling and de-limbing roles, changing forever the centuries-old domination of axe and manual saw.

The horse was the pre-eminent means of hauling timber from the felling site to the roadside right up until 1960 when 53 per cent of the Forestry Commission's production was still handled in this way. The introduction of tractors had already displaced horses from much of lowland England where they were able to operate on the easier terrain, but the horse's ability to work efficiently in hilly country where wheeled vehicles could not venture ensured their continuing role. Average annual volume of timber extracted by a horse was about 1,000 cubic metres. The horses were generally Clydesdales or Garrons and were almost all privately owned, hauling timber with their owners who had to ensure their care and well-being seven days a week. Simple chain and harness systems were in general use for hauling of timber. More sophisticated systems were brought in from Scandinavia, but by that time the role of the horse had largely been taken over by tractors or cable crane winching systems. By 1969 only 14 per cent of the Forestry Commission's timber in Britain was still being extracted by horses and only 38 horses were being used in England, mainly in the hill country of Northumberland and Cumbria. Nowadays, horses are once again used, albeit on a very small scale, to extract timber from some of the most sensitive sites where heavy wheeled equipment might damage sensitive plants or habitats such as the woodlands that provide a home to the nightingale in East Anglia.

Tractors had begun to be introduced seriously for timber extraction in the Second World War. Heavy crawlers had been used for the clear-felling of large trees, but the Forestry Commission's timber harvest was mainly of thinnings so it was light agricultural tractors that took over from horses on the easier terrain. The number of tractors increased by almost 50 per cent between 1960 and 1969. As with chainsaws there was a strong focus on improvement of equipment and techniques in order to boost productivity. Terrain ability was improved by the addition of wheel-chains, but the main change was the addition of winches, which meant that the tractor could be parked in an appropriate location in the woodland, and the felled poles could be drawn towards it using the winch rope.

In these early days, large-scale timber harvesting in British forests was starting from scratch and the inventiveness and ingenuity of the Forestry Commission's teams led the way in machinery design when suitable equipment could not be sourced at home or abroad. During the 1970s, the Forestry Commission's Mechanical Engineers designed and commissioned their own 'skidders' – tractors which pull timber along the ground. Their innovative design was based on a commercially available four-wheel-drive unit, but adapted with wheels, log-rolling blade, winches, guarding and protective cab specifically to operate in British forestry conditions. The Eggesford and Malvern were the early variants but the later Falstone skidder became ubiquitous as the machine of choice for timber extraction across the Forestry Commission. They took their innovation even further into groundbreaking territory with a frame-steered tractor employing hydrostatic drive and radio controlled winches that won the 'Most Outstanding Machine in Show' award at the 1974 Royal Agricultural Show and went into commercial production in partnership with a tractor manufacturer as the Logmaster.

The skidder operator worked as part of the team with the chainsaw operators cross-cutting at the roadside. Good coordination was the key to efficient working and good piecework outputs. Later, the skidder fleet was supplemented by large Timberjack skidders brought in from Canada and purpose-built for hauling timber in the forest. These machines were capable of much higher outputs than previous machines and this required careful planning so as not to overwhelm the roadside cross-cutting team.

For steep, wet and very rough ground, the revolution that was to finally displace the horse came with the winch and cable crane introduced in the mid-1960s. A tractor was equipped with a tower and winches to provide the roadside base for a winch-rope system that could go anywhere to extract timber. The early Isachsen winches were very simple with a limited range of around 150 metres and hauled out the trees with one end dragging along the ground. With the development of skyline systems where a tensioned fixed rope was suspended above the ground with a carriage to carry the load, the range was extended up to 600 metres. The cable crane was worked by a crew of two communicating with use of two-way radio. The 'winch man' was at the roadside operating the winch controls while the 'choker man' was on the hill attaching the felled trees to the winch rope.

Mechanisation also had a big impact on silvicultural operations. A history of the Whitelee Forest south of Glasgow describes the 'cutting-edge' machinery that began to be employed in the 1960s, using two tractors to pull a plough over the deep peat, the first tractor to pull the plough and the second to pull the tractor out when it sunk. Helicopters began to be employed to scatter fertiliser rock dust. Prior to this, a forestry worker might be expected to pick up a hundredweight bag of rock phosphate from the roadside to act as fertiliser, then carry it on his back over rough ground for 10 kilometres to the planting site. To cover a whole landscape took weeks of backbreaking work from whole teams of men whereas, breathtakingly, a helicopter could do the same work in one afternoon.

# The 1970s

Despite the increasing volume of timber production through the 1960s, a review of forestry policy including a cost-benefit study was announced by ministers in December 1970. The economic analysis in the study concluded that the creation of State forests was uneconomic. However, the government decided that the social benefits of forestry, such as job creation, had been given too little weight. They decided on a reduced planting programme, focusing on areas of greater unemployment. Luckily, the impact of the review was limited as planting programmes were already largely concentrated in these areas, but this was a worrying time for the Commission.

The decade saw real highs, but also lows. On a positive note, the Commission appointed its first female forester in 1976, as well as the first batch of resident artists at Grizedale in 1977. This theme is explored at length in The Arts in the Forest p.183. However, the 1970s was also the decade when the national tree stock was hit by Dutch elm disease. This virulent disease spread across the country, devastating the landscape and

*Grizedale Forest Visitor Centre, date unknown*

causing a huge amount of worry and work for staff in the Commission as they sought to fight back. The damaging environmental impact led to a government campaign called Plant a Tree in '73. The front-line measures undertaken by Commission staff to fight the disease led to a greater awareness of the work that they undertook, in particular that of Forest Research. Indeed, when the Commission celebrated the 25th anniversary of its research station Alice Holt in 1972 by throwing its doors open to the public, more than 3,000 people attended over the course of two days.

## The Leisure Industry

By 1970, the Commission had hit 15 million day visitors, as well as one million annual camping trips, with further increases during the decade. National Forest Parks had first been created back in the 1930s and the National Parks of England and Wales had been created by an Act of Parliament in 1949, but it was in the 1960s and 1970s that the leisure industry really came into its own, with much cheaper, and therefore more widespread, car ownership fuelling the desire to explore. The 1968 Countryside Act in England and Wales, and the 1967 Countryside Act in Scotland, had encouraged the opening up of the countryside for recreation and gave the Commission powers to provide facilities to support this. The 1973 *Forest Recreation Handbook*, published for Forestry Commission staff, set out the policy to 'develop its forests for recreation' with a broad recreation focus including access on foot free of charge, interpretation, car parks, visitor centres, forest drives, overnight accommodation, field sports, fishing, orienteering, horseriding, motor sports and education. This inclusive approach has continued to the present day.

During the 1970s, new facilities for the public visitor were being steadily built, with the Forest Cabins Branch being formed to oversee the building of new holiday cabins. The building of cabins sowed the seeds of later overnight recreational access. The new powers granted by the 1967 and 1968 Countryside Acts saw the conversion of spare workers' houses to cottages and four cabin sites between 1972 and 1980 at Deer Park in Cornwall, Keldy in North Yorkshire, and Strathyre and Loch Awe in Scotland, in addition to the already established campsites across

Great Britain. This provided, at the time, an almost unique experience and these four cabin sites remained in direct management of the Forestry Commission until 2006, when a new partnership was put in place with the Camping and Caravanning Club (CCC) to manage and expand the overnight accommodation provision in the forest. This then evolved in 2012 to two new partnerships, Camping in the Forest with the CCC and Forest Holidays with a new investment partner. From 2006, new cabins were built in Hampshire, the Forest of Dean, North Yorkshire, Nottinghamshire and Argyll, and today there are ten sites across Great Britain, each of which, as well as providing great holidays, creates on average 60 all-year-round jobs in the local rural economy, mostly for young people, and provides valuable long-term income to Forestry England, Natural Resources Wales and Forestry and Land Scotland supporting their ongoing management of the UK's public forests.

## Further Advances in Mechanisation

Following the introduction of some cutting-edge machinery in the 1960s (see Early Mechanisation, p.63), the next stage in the mechanisation of forestry came in timber harvesting based on the development of the hydraulic crane and grapple. As lorries began to be fitted with the new equipment, the first area to benefit was timber haulage, and more particularly the forest workers who had been loading timber products by hand. While the larger sawlogs had previously been loaded mainly by independent timber cranes using wire ropes and slings, smaller dimension products such as pulpwood and pit wood were loaded by hand. Seventy per cent of Forestry Commission produce had been loaded by hand in 1960, rapidly reducing to 39 per cent by 1969 and largely disappearing by the mid-1970s. The size of timber lorries has increased in line with road transport legislation and they have become increasingly specialised over the years. Many Forestry Commission forests operated their own lorries until the 1980s after which this activity became entirely a contract operation.

In the 1970s 'forwarders' were introduced to the UK from Scandinavia. These machines were purpose-built for forestry conditions and combined a cab unit and trailer, a hydraulic crane and grapple, with six or eight wheels and an articulated centre joint. They brought with them a completely new way of working whereby all the cross-cutting into timber products by the tree fellers was done in the forest where the tree was felled. The forwarder was then able to collect the products from the felling site, take them out to the forest road, and stack them ready for collection by lorry. As specialised vehicles, the forwarders had great terrain capability, especially when fitted with flotation tyres and band tracks to spread their weight.

This new way of working where the timber products were prepared at the felling site was called 'short wood' and replaced the previously prevalent 'pole length' working where the de-limbed whole trees were extracted for cross-cutting at the roadside. It brought the added benefit that the timber products were much cleaner than with the skidder systems where the trees were dragged along the ground gathering soil and stones as they went. To ensure that the new forwarders could operate efficiently,

*Lining-out machine and transplant trays. Wykeham Nursery, North Yorkshire, 1971*

the tree-felling methods needed to change. Organised felling systems were introduced to create zones of timber products and zones of branch wood that supported the travel of the forwarder on wet ground. At the same time a variant of organised felling was introduced for steep-ground working. In 'contour felling' the trees are felled in a systematic way – a proportion at right angles to the contour to act as benches down which the remaining trees can be rolled as they are felled along the contour to form separate branchwood and produce zones to increase the output of cable cranes. These systems are safer and less physically demanding, but the change called for new skills on the part of chainsaw operators and intensive training by the Forestry Commission's Education and Training Branch. Specialist teams were set up to train on chainsaws while new organised tree-felling techniques and 'trainability' tests were developed to identify those best suited to develop their skills in new directions. The depth, value and quality of this training are still highly regarded by those who were involved – particularly the three-week basic chainsaw course that equipped people not just to fell a tree safely but also to set out with confidence into the world of timber harvesting on piecework.

The final phase of mechanisation of timber harvesting again drew on Scandinavian experience where, with the challenge of a vast forest harvest, engineers were working on developing the forwarder base unit to undertake the remaining manual elements of timber harvesting. The first step, in the late 1970s, was the 'timber processor' which was able to travel into the forest to carry out de-limbing of the felled trees, cross-cutting them into products and stacking them ready for extraction by the forwarder. It was only a short step from there to develop the processors by adding a tree-felling function to the crane and the mechanisation of the timber harvesting process was complete. The first harvesters were introduced in the 1980s and were able to fell, debranch and cross-cut trees into a range of sizes and diameters. Now nearly all the British timber harvest is undertaken by timber harvesters working with forwarders and the operating technology and systems are well established. They can operate on slopes and terrain that would have been thought impossible 30 years ago. Depending on tree size, each harvester fells between 30,000 and 55,000 cubic metres of timber per year, felling, de-limbing and cross-cutting a tree in less than a minute. Work that at one time would have required 30 or more chainsaw operators can now be carried out with a level of precision, efficiency, and operator safety and welfare that could not have been imagined 50 years ago. Only the steepest ground and the largest coniferous and broadleaved trees require the highly skilled manual input that is now sadly in very short supply.

# The 1980s

This decade was one of huge change for the Forestry Commission. The country was in deep recession in the early 1980s and cutbacks were being made across government. In 1980 a review of forestry policy was launched. Despite broadly supporting the existing forestry policy and commitment to new planting, the Commission was still heavily reliant on government funding and the review concluded that it should sell off a proportion of its land to reduce the need for grant aid. The Bill was a controversial one but passed as the 1981 Forestry Act: 180,000 hectares of land were sold between 1981 and 1994, reducing the proportion of State-owned woodlands from 50 to 37 per cent. However, increasing opposition to sales led the government to halt privatisation in 1994 and the decision was made for the Commission's woodlands to remain in public hands 'at this stage in their development', although sales of smaller land parcels continued, in an ill-conceived approach to balancing the books, until the second decade of the 21st century.

## The Impact of Mechanisation

Mechanisation delivered the efficiency drive needed for the industry but it came at a cost, leading to the loss of many manual jobs and often, as with mining and traditional manufacturing, the break-up of long-existing communities. The mechanisation of forestry meant that the job of 20–30 men could eventually be done by two, one in a harvester and the other in a timber transport machine such as a tractor driver with trailer or a forwarder. Thousands of men were eventually made redundant, with the workforce falling from a peak of 15,500 in the mid-1950s to only

7,950 by 1981. This made some workers extremely bitter and resentful at the Commission for not doing more to prevent their way of life from being destroyed. It was a difficult time for the Commission in many ways as it was made to focus on its core economics, almost completely moving away from its other original purpose of keeping large numbers of people employed in the countryside, and this before its other key aims of conservation and recreation really came to the fore in the mid- to late 1980s.

Some communities, such as that in Kielder Forest, found the transition to mechanisation traumatic because the culture of work was ruptured. In others, such as Thetford Forest, the workforce was managed down and allowed to transition more organically. The areas most affected were those where the Forestry Commission was the only employer, such as the remoter areas of Scotland, or where previous agricultural land had been turned over to forestry and as a result there were no manual jobs in farming to turn to.

For some, however, it was a great opportunity to increase income. Some forest workers bought their own chainsaws once they became affordable. Many went into contracting work in the private sector, where they sacrificed the security and comforting arm of the Forestry Commission in order to make a higher wage. A skilled woodsman could earn five times his salary in the private sector by fully employing his skills and modern technology, as a former employee explains:

> Because I was being paid to get the job done it meant I could invest in the most efficient machinery, stuff I'd known about but had no use for in the FC. If you're restricted to felling, say, 50 trees and your pay is fixed you're not going to splash out on your own chainsaw to do it any faster. Once I was getting paid for the whole job I was going to do that as fast as I could and move on.

Innovation was driven by forestry contractors competing with each other. If one group mechanised then their output would go up, so their competitiveness could go up to win contracts and their ability to achieve more work in the same time meant that wages went up.

The same worker describes the change in attitude that resulted:

Before, if the boss came to inspect the woods, one of the boys would be expected to stay and wash the man's car while he was being taken for the tour. It really was like that! The day I went private that all changed, now we were just two men engaged in negotiations. I was no longer just Munroe to be sent here or there to do this or that, now I was *Mr* Munroe. I liked it! And once I had the contract that's what we stuck to. I found it very empowering.

## Privatisation of Housing

Another significant change during this period was the privatisation of the housing stock. As mechanisation led to a decline in the size of the workforce, the Commission ceased to build new homes and the housing stock was gradually sold off throughout the 1970s and 1980s. Key holdings were reserved, though, for Wildlife Rangers, and the Forestry Commission still maintains a number of houses, particularly in strategic locations and for key staff.

As the availability of housing dried up, many foresters did not get a forester's cottage when they were on their specialist tours of duty. People could therefore be on and off the housing ladder several times, and asked to go to locations at short notice where the pay was exactly the same but the cost of housing was several times higher. Again, conditions were different in different districts of the country. Workers in more populated areas had more options for accommodation but with greater expense, and they were less likely to be part of a forest community; those in more remote locations had fewer options when subsidised accommodation was withdrawn. Some were able to retire and allowed to stay living in tied accommodation until their death, and that also applied to their partner. It was different in southern England, where a key house would be kept open for an incumbent forester or member of staff.

The era of privatisation in the 1980s resulted in many forest districts outsourcing their labour force to carry out harvesting contracts very early on, even where it did not necessarily make economic sense to do so. Eventually this resulted in almost all harvesting on the forest estate being done under tendered contract. But there are also strong examples of districts working differently because it made sense for them to do so at the time. In the north-east of Scotland for example, the district expended a considerable amount of time and effort in the 1980s building up its own in-house harvesting and marketing team and mechanising it, because the region was so particularly vulnerable to the loss of contracted labour to the North Sea oil and gas industry.

## Restructuring the Forests

The transformation of the Commission's forests which had begun in the 1960s continued through restructuring plans first developed for the North York Moors and Kielder in the 1980s. Restructuring took the relatively uniform forest that had resulted from the early plantings and broke it up into smaller individual felling areas or 'coupes' that were of an appropriate scale for the landscape and which were bounded as far as possible by roads, rides, open space and streams to give the best chance of a wind-firm edge. These shapes would then be replanted, but with the creation of more open space and with planting kept back from their boundary to create more space for wildlife and more interesting and wind-firm forest edges throughout the forest. The intention was that there would be at least a ten-year age gap between adjacent coupes. This meant that some trees would be harvested earlier or later than their economic felling age, but the overall effect would be a more varied, uneven aged, attractive and more stable forest.

In the 1980s the first Forest Design Plan (now called Forest Plan) was developed for Ennerdale in the Lake District – the planning process integrated landscape design with other aspects of forest management such as recreation and conservation and has been evolving ever since. Forest Plans set out management policies and plans as a long-term vision for every forest for the next 50 years. The felling and thinning plans show clearly where timber will be harvested, and the replanting plan sets out how and where the next generation of trees will be planted or naturally regenerated. These Forest Plans are fed in to the Production Forecast and form the basis of timber harvesting programmes. Alongside the felling and replanting plans, the Forest Plans include proposals for forest recreation and for conservation management. Today, the whole of the Forestry Commission's estate is covered by Forest Plans. They have evolved over time and are now made available for public consultation and are reviewed and updated every ten years.

## Developments in Conservation

The Wildlife and Countryside Act of 1981 introduced new protections for both plants and animals and instigated a new balance between timber production and conservation. Changes to the Forestry Commission's role in countryside management, particularly with regard to wildlife through the mid–late 1980s to the modern day, meant that it started to attract different people into its wildlife-focused roles. This helped to accelerate the pace of change to one where wildlife became extremely highly valued and the Commission is now one of the leading examples of conservation theory, policy and practice in the UK. Many of the Commission's staff had long been ahead of their time in taking steps to benefit wildlife – such as ride-side enhancement or enhancing a pond and hiding this work as part of routine ditch maintenance or road maintenance – and the Commission was quick to adopt new policies and approaches as conservation became an accepted and established role for government.

Progressive reform has changed the role of the Commission into one of conservationist. Deer culling is still necessary – their unnaturally high population densities are considered by leading ecologists to be one of the most significant factors in degrading woodland habitats and in the conservation status of many woodland species, in addition to the threat they present to establishing and regenerating young trees for any purpose. But the Commission has also played a leading role in the protection and even the reintroduction of many species, including red squirrels, white-tailed sea eagles, beavers, butterflies and spiders, and has become one of the leading forces for conservation in the UK.

Mark Warn, Dorset Wildlife Ranger explains:

I think there has been a significant change in the attitude of the Forestry Commission over its history with regard to wildlife from one of a follower working to the statutory requirements of conservation and animal welfare to being a real leader in those fields. There is no question that in the time I have been working we used to be public enemy number one because we had planted the heaths with trees and were therefore responsible, along with agriculture and urban expansion, for the decline of lowland heath. We really listened to that and took it on the chin and have since delivered a huge amount of heathland restoration work. We changed the way we work so that we kept on delivering timber production but also really deliver conservation in a much more financially sustainable way than most of the other projects I have been aware of. Giving really high environmental benefits for a very low unit price, to the extent that many of our strongest critics are now holding us up as an example of how to deliver practical conservation. Wareham [Forest] is now probably *the* most important site in the country for heathland reptiles thanks to the efforts of the Forestry Commission and conservation bodies recognise that the whole forest delivers for those species, not just the pristine untouched heathland parts.

The Commission's increasing role as a conservationist extended beyond just wildlife. Having acquired huge areas of land for planting, it is unsurprising that it also became the custodian of thousands of important heritage assets dating from early periods of prehistory to silos and bunkers from the Cold War era. Concerns about protecting these assets had been expressed in the 1930s but reached a head in the 1970s and 1980s as attitudes towards wider countryside management were changing. The Commission appointed a series of external consultants to advise on these issues in the mid-1980s leading to the appointment of its first archaeologist, although the role was more broadly about the historic environment and landscape than strictly archaeology. Standards for new planting were set for protecting the historic environment which had to be met to qualify for grant aid and these days there are active programmes of site conservation and research underway together with many interpretation projects. Volunteers play an important role in many projects, including examination of the evidence gathered from Lidar surveys which have revealed past landscapes beneath the tree cover.

## Challenges to Plantation Forestry

As awareness of wildlife and the wider environment grew, this began to influence the Forestry Commission's planting policies. During the 1960s and 1970s there had been growing concern over the impact of government support for the conversion of largely broadleaf woods to coniferous plantations. The plantings of the Commission between the wars had been largely focused on bare land often in the uplands or on very low-quality agricultural land. Following the Second World War, with land prices higher and increasing support for private landowners, conversion of broadleaf woods became more common. Much of the woodland cover of England was described as 'derelict woodland'. Following the experience of the world wars, the idea that it was in the public interest to bring these woods into production was not an unreasonable one. Nevertheless there is no doubt that this publicly subsidised and well-meaning enthusiasm went too far. Against this background a reaction took hold. The inspiring work of naturalist Oliver Rackham, others in the Nature Conservancy, and people like woodland ecologist George Peterken to protect these old woods was important as well as successful. The term 'Ancient Woodland' was coined to describe the valuable habitats contained in these under-managed woods and recognise their historical and environmental significance. In 1985, following a government review, the Broadleaved Woodland Policy was published. In a statement, the Secretary of State for Scotland noted that 'encouragement will be given to the greater use of broadleaved woodlands generally for conservation, recreation, sport and landscape as well as for wood production' and that 'steps will be taken to ensure that the special interest of the ancient semi-natural woodlands is recognised and maintained'. This was superseded by the Woodland Grant Scheme of 2003, the multiple aims of which were timber production, improvements in the landscape, opportunities for recreation, and the provision of new habitats for wildlife. In recent years there has been considerable interest in identifying and prioritising Plantations on Ancient Woodland Sites (PAWS), and the Commission has a long-term programme of converting such sites back to native woodland species. Planting of broadleaves has increased dramatically rising from 6 per cent of restocking planting in England in 1978 to 30 per cent in 2018.

The concerns about Ancient Woodland in southern England were echoed later in the 1980s by concerns over private planting on ecologically sensitive sites and the consequences of the generous tax reliefs on planting. One of the most notorious examples of this practice took place in the Flow Country, an area of peatland in Caithness and Sutherland in north-east Scotland which was rich in native wildlife. The area was extensively drained and planted with conifers, and this had a devastating effect on wildlife and radically changed the ecology of the area. The planting in the Flow Country was supported by tax breaks for largely absentee investors. This was brought to a head with a very public campaign by the RSPB and some very high-profile investors including the well-known radio and television personality Terry Wogan. In his 1988 budget Chancellor Nigel Lawson took commercial woodlands out of the income tax system altogether so that expenditure on commercial woodlands would no longer be allowed as a deduction for income tax and corporation tax. The tax relief on planting was replaced by grants which strongly favoured broadleaves, leading to a sudden collapse in new commercial planting. In the Flow Country itself, public funds once used to support inappropriate planting have now been used to attempt to restore the original landscape, and conservation groups such as the RSPB have also bought land in the area. This painful episode was a real turning point for the Forestry Commission. The original exclusive focus on maximising the timber yield by industrial plantation of conifer blocks had evolved and softened in various ways over the decades, but it was now apparent that striking a better balance between the interests of timber production, conservation and recreation was absolutely imperative to the Commission's reputation and its very survival.

Unfortunately, the decade ended in devastation for woodlands across the south-east of England. In October 1987, the region was hit by near-hurricane-force winds. The Great Storm blew down over 15 million trees with the majority of damage in hedgerows, private gardens and woodlands, and around 25 per cent in Forestry Commission woodlands. The sheer scale of damage was unprecedented and trees of great personal or scientific value, including many at Bedgebury Pinetum, were lost. It took until 1990 to clear the harvestable blown timber and the scars are still visible. Nevertheless, the impact of the storm taught woodland managers important lessons which are still influencing planning today. At Bedgebury Pinetum, for example, Norway spruces have been planted as windbreaks on more exposed slopes and planting schemes have moved from single species to become more mixed.

# The 1990s

By the 1990s, the concept of multipurpose forestry had become integral to the Commission's work. The potential benefit of woodlands and forests to urban communities was increasingly recognised at this time, with funds made available to support the development of the National Forest, the Central Scotland Woodlands and the Community Forests in England, and new incentives introduced to improve public access to private woodlands. The decade also saw a boost in timber production. Consumption of wood products in Britain had been increasing and, from 1993 to 2000, annual production from the Commission's forests rose from 4 million cubic metres to over 5 million.

## Changing Roles

In 1992, the Forestry Commission was reformed and internally divided to create a branch that was much more focused and dedicated to private-sector woodland than had previously been the case. This was originally called the Forestry Authority and was later rebranded in England as Forest Services during another reorganisation.

There was also increased training available to managers on people skills and motivation. John Weir, a forester in Scotland at the time, recalls that 'you could feel things changing in the 1980s. I remember they held training courses in Edinburgh, two blocks of two weeks, on how to manage people and all these different types of motivational techniques and people management styles. All new entrant foresters were put on those courses in large cohorts, from all over the country.'

Reorganisation placed District Officers (who were also renamed Forest Officers) in the same offices as the other workers, removing one of the middle layers of management. Much larger blocks of forests called Forest Districts were formed, meaning many of the Head and Chief Forester roles went too. Class barriers were also broken down and some of the foresters who came through at this key time of change went on to hold some of the most senior jobs in the Forestry Commission. They had been all the way through the ranks and understood the details of the core business as well as management, so they were held in high esteem by many of the staff inside the organisation and were able to lead the organisation as it changed focus through the late 1980s to the modern day.

## Forest Recreation

The 1980s and 1990s also saw the start of new trends in forest recreation: the appointment of professional staff to manage and deliver recreation; the diversification of the offer with children's play and mountain biking; and the development of more recreation facilities closer to urban populations. The Community Forests in England set out ambitious plans to create more forests on the urban fringe and also to restore former brownfield land and create green lungs for the cities. On the Forestry Commission estate, 'Woodland Parks' were designated in the smaller forests closer to urban centres with a remit to provide more recreation opportunities. Later, there was a drive to provide more access in privately owned woodland with the development of grants and the Woodland Welcome Scheme in 2002.

In the late 1980s the Countryside Commission had run a competition to select an area of England for the creation of a new 'National Forest' close to communities to improve the environment and provide access for public recreation. An area of 518 square kilometres from Leicestershire to Staffordshire was selected due to its low woodland cover at around 6 per cent in an area heavily impacted by mining and quarrying activity. In 1995 the National Forest Company was formed to lead the forest creation, working with local authorities, landowners, the Forestry Commission and other agencies. By the end of the 1990s 3.2 million trees had been planted and woodland cover had almost doubled to 11.2 per cent.

Direct funding from the Forestry Commission was becoming more scarce. An internal circular of 1980 had stated that 'priority in the allocation of limited resources available for recreation will be given to the maintenance of existing facilities to a high standard'. At the same time there was a growing recognition across the sector that forest recreation was here to stay. In 1992 the first Forest Recreation guidelines were published as part of a suite of guidance for forest managers in the public and private sectors. These guidelines recognised the value of woodlands and also the management of different activities to meet visitors' needs, generating income from recreation and protecting the forest environment. At this time commercial recreation on Forestry Commission land was largely associated with cabins, campsites and holiday cottages, bringing in around £3.2 million of income with a review focusing solely on these elements of recreation. This approach changed over the next decade as income from parking, cafés and bike hire began to grow and a broader approach to commercial recreation developed.

Mapping of Forestry Commission woodlands in the early 1990s as part of the Ramblers' Atlas was also important in further establishing recreation as a key feature of the organisation's activity and a major factor in pressure on the government to abandon the sell-off of the Forestry Commission landholding introduced under the Forestry Act 1981.

## Communities and Volunteers

As recreation became more formalised across the Commission's forests, the enthusiasm from local people wishing to develop their woodlands and forests grew exponentially. Volunteers had played an important role on the public forest estate for a number of decades – the Bedgebury Arboretum Committee was meeting as far back as 1942 – but it was in the 1990s that volunteering became more formalised. The Forestry Commission saw the benefits of involving local people, and groups became empowered to take on a more active role in developing their forests. Whether as individuals coming together to construct bespoke cycle trails down their favourite hillside, relabel an arboretum collection, or set up initiatives to improve health and well-being, people wanted to get involved. The Commission began to realise the importance of the added benefits volunteers could bring and it wasn't long before volunteer programmes, recruitment drives and formal recognition schemes became common practice.

As people became more empowered and passionate about the surrounding countryside and the woodlands they visited, so their expectations of how these areas should be managed grew. The Forestry Commission embraced this enthusiasm and encouraged individuals and groups to become more involved in land management. In the rugged western valleys of Cumbria, for example, volunteers have played an essential role in habitat restoration as part of the Wild Ennerdale partnership project. With a passionate focus on restoring natural processes and increasing the sense of wildness, the project has gathered significant local interest, with volunteers wanting to give something back to their local area and share their skills. They have also become brilliant advocates for this type of innovative land management and are a sounding board for how local people will feel about new ideas. The tasks carried out by volunteer groups are also particularly valuable as they often have a relatively low impact on surrounding habitats. This sensitivity is particularly important in Sites of Special Scientific Interest (SSSIs) or for remote tasks that contractors would struggle to access or that would be financially unviable for them to take on due to the imposed environmental constraints. From woodland to heathland, clearing rides to removing invasive species, sustainable land management became an important part of volunteer programmes.

The consolidation of urban and community forestry in the 1990s and 2000s also marked a significant change to the way in which the Commission engaged with communities. In community woodlands and partnership projects, often nestled in urban areas of deprivation, the restoration of landscapes enabled woodland access for a greater proportion of the population. Community members and volunteers were directly involved from the outset, influencing the design of these spaces. Funding for these projects, for example from Regional Development Agencies (RDAs), often gave staff the financial ability to engage directly with local people to educate, inspire and involve them in their transformed environment. Sutton Manor, a former colliery pit outside St Helens, was taken on by the Forestry Commission in 2001, funded by the Capital Modernisation Fund. The local community, which included a number of ex-miners who had worked on the site as an operational colliery, was hugely influential in the design. While early concept designs had been largely productive conifer planting, the community wanted a more open feel to the woodland with ponds and wetlands. As a result, the final planting plan had a roughly 60 per cent woodland to 40 per cent open space mix and has been extremely popular with the local community.

These volunteer programmes have also been a huge asset in inspiring engagement with the outdoors and providing work experience and training opportunities for groups that would not normally consider a career in forestry. Volunteers include GP referrals, carers empowering patients, excluded students, and unemployed people seeking skills training. Rangers have also worked with colleges, faith groups and the British Red Cross, leading skills training programmes and enabling new sectors of society to engage with the nation's forests.

## International Certification

Sustainable forestry management, balancing environmental, social and economic concerns, became a dominant part of the forestry policy during the 1990s and this was reflected in the publication of the UK Forestry Standard (UKFS) in 1998. This defined the UK government's approach to sustainable forest management and brought various technical guidelines and regulations into one codified document that unified forestry practices across the UK and provided a basis for international reporting. It also now underpins the Forest Plans across the public forest estate. Globally, independent certification of forest management was developed in the 1990s to provide assurance to consumers about the sustainability of timber against a background of increasing concern about global loss of forests and bad practice in forest management and timber harvesting. The UK launched the UK Woodland Assurance Standard in 1999, endorsed by the Forest Stewardship Council® (FSC®). Later that year, and after eight months of rigorous independent audit, the whole of the Forestry Commission estate was awarded FSC certification. As the first State forest in the world to be FSC-certified, this set the Commission as a leader on the global stage, with independent confirmation that its forest management and the timber produced met the highest environmental, social and economic standards. The presentation of the prestigious WWF Gift to the Earth award to the Forestry Commission in 2001 recognised this achievement in forest certification and good forest management. All the Commission's timber production carries the FSC label (and latterly the Programme for the Endorsement of Forest Certification™ [PEFC™] label in addition) as confirmation that it has been grown and harvested in well-managed forests. Certification has rapidly become a prerequisite for the sale of timber to large-scale processors and has been maintained for the Forestry Commission estate through regular audit over the past 20 years.

# The 21st Century

The turn of the century saw the Commission responding to unprecedented change and challenges, with the proposed sell-off of public forests and the devolution of forestry to England and Wales. It also became more important than ever to plan for the future as the threat of climate change became clear. In 2009 the Commission produced the Read Report, an independent assessment examining the potential of the UK's trees and woodlands to mitigate and adapt to a changing climate. The study is considered to be the first national assessment of its kind in the world and attracted interest from other countries keen to form their own climate change plans and policies.

## Staff Unification

As the Forestry Commission approached the millennium, the staffing structures that had been in place since its inception were no longer fit for purpose. The days of large gangs of workers planting trees or harvesting timber on piecework were over, and the nature of the work and the skills required had become much more wide-ranging. The division of the staff into 'officers and men' or 'blue collar and white collar' was no longer appropriate to meeting the new challenges that it faced. The incoming Director-General David Bills, an Australian who had joined the Forestry Commission with a wealth of international experience, could see this very clearly and set about removing the anachronistic division between the 'industrial' and 'non-industrial' workforce. He was firm in his belief that the Commission needed to be able to harness the skills, experience and energy of all its people working together in common cause, enjoying fair pay and conditions and, importantly, being able to feel equal respect for the contribution that they were making to the Commission's current activities and future ambitions. On 27 June 2000, the Forestry Commission's trade unions announced that their members had voted convincingly to accept a package of new conditions of service. This enabled the implementation of a unified staff group on 1 July, and contributed to the achievement of 'Investors in People' status later in the year. The importance of what might seem to be a simple set of technical changes to pay and conditions for staff cannot be overstated. The common level of recognition and respect by the Forestry Commission for its entire staff was the springboard to the development of the new culture and way of working that would prove essential as the Commission evolved to find its unique place in meeting the new demands and challenges of the 21st century.

Dry Stone Passage. *Sculpture by Richard Harris, Grizedale Forest, 1982*

## Meeting People's Needs

Recreation continued to be a success for the Forestry Commission which by the 1990s had become the largest single provider of outdoor recreation in the UK. The 2003 Land Reform Act in Scotland and 2000 Countryside and Rights of Way Act (known as the CROW Act) in England and Wales gave the public right of access to 'open country' or registered common land. The public had been given the right to roam in the Commission's forests in the 1960s but these Acts enshrined public access to them in law rather than simply as a permitted activity. To this day, most of the visits to the nation's forests are for a simple walk in the woods. The forests of England, Scotland and Wales are crisscrossed with trails offering everything from quiet riverside strolls to hikes up to stunning viewpoints.

Work on the National Forest continued through the early part of the 21st century: in addition to increasing woodland cover in the area to 20.7 per cent and planting a total of 8.7 million trees, there were landmark investments in public recreation. In 2011 the Forestry Commission's National Forest Cycle Centre at Hicks Lodge was opened. The National Forest took its place on the map with the opening of a 75-mile long-distance walking trail in 2014: the National Forest Way.

In England there was increasingly a recognition that forest recreation was in a competitive market with other leisure activities and that it could also help to contribute to the Commission's finances. Along with significant grants available from the EU and the National Lottery, the 2000s saw significant growth in the recreation offer and increasing partnerships with private business. Growth of mountain biking, children's play, Go Ape high ropes courses, investment in car parking, cafés, toilets and trails led to increasing visitor numbers, tripling income from recreation in a ten-year period to comprise up to 25 per cent of the total income generated. The culmination of the growth of formal and informal recreation work in England has led to an estimated 226 million visits to the estate in 2017/18. Scotland focused heavily on increasing access in urban areas through the Woods In and Around Towns initiative. Better understanding of customers' needs and the increasing reputation of the Forestry Commission as an important outdoor recreation provider have led to greater investment in marketing campaigns and partnerships targeting key audiences who are less likely to be visiting forests. The best known example of this approach has been the long-running partnership with Magic Light and Julia Donaldson, including the award-winning Gruffalo Trail with the Gruffalo app which has attracted 1.67 million visits across England. Working with Sport England, the Forestry Commission has also developed new programmes to increase the number of sporting visits to the estate, with running becoming a key activity.

The Forestry Commission's concert programme had started at the end of the 1980s inspired by Mike Taylor's vision to get more people to visit High Lodge forest centre in Thetford Forest. Working from 2001 with industry expert David Barrow, Mike then pioneered the Forest Tour, bringing together a group of sites to create what is now the Forestry Commission Forest Live music programme. Artists have included Jools Holland, Paul Weller, Simply Red, Paloma Faith, Plan B and Massive Attack. Pulp played a concert at Culbin Forest in 2002, the first and only time the tour ventured into Scotland. With over one million visitors over the 17 seasons of the concert programme, it has achieved Mike's vision to get more people to visit the forest and created amazing nights out under the trees for hundreds of thousands of people.

Children's play has been an important element of the Forestry Commission's recreation offer. The use of natural play spaces and timber had been recognised in the 1980s in the Countryside Commission Scotland and Forestry Commission guidance *Providing for Children's Play in the Countryside* and influenced early play trails at Moors Valley and other locations and the partnership with Andy Frost whose iconic play sculptures became key features at many forests. The 2000s saw a renaissance of play as both a positive element of children's development and an appreciation of the value of nature in addressing increasing mental and physical health problems in children and teenagers. Working with child expert Tim Gill, the Commission developed a fresh approach to children's play captured in a series of reports and guidance based around the theme of growing adventure. This led to new nature play spaces across the country and helped encourage many children to get out into the forest.

Forest Education became a more important feature of the public offer during the 1990s with the appointment of a national Education Officer and the development of the Forest Education Initiative and a British version of the Danish Forest School concept. Forest Enterprise England launched its first national learning strategy on World Forestry Day, 21 March 2013, celebrated with events in 36 different forests, attended by a total of more than 1,000 learners. As a result now 150 learning permissions set up across England reach well over 100,000 learners per year.

Off-road cycling has taken place since bicycles were invented and the Rough Stuff Fellowship had pioneered off-road cycling from their first formal outing near Bolton in 1955. Mountain biking really started to emerge in the late 1980s. Early approaches were to manage access through a permissions system but this was soon abandoned and the early 1990s saw the development of waymarked trails largely on the Forest Road network. While these trails were welcomed, many mountain bikers wanted more technical trails and Forestry Commission pioneers Dafydd Davis and Karl Bartlett responded to this at Coed y Brenin in Wales and Mabie Forest in Scotland and Firecrest Mountain Biking's Ian Warby at Aston Hill in England. As the level of activity grew, the 7stanes project in Scotland created a network of trails across the south of the country in 2002–04 to help rebuild tourism after the foot-and-mouth epidemic and the Welsh government made a strategic investment in mountain bike centres in forests to boost Welsh tourism. This included Coed y Brenin Forest Park, Afan Forest Park, Cwmcarn Forest Drive, Bwlch Nant yr Arian and the Tilhill/One Planet Adventure managed bike park at Llandegla Forest, among others. Development in England has been more focused on easier trails for families and leisure cyclists but has also delivered world-class trails. Dalby Forest in North Yorkshire hosted the Union Cycliste Internationale (UCI) Mountain Bike Cross Country World Cup for the first time in 2010. Around 7 per cent of all visits to Commission land now include a bike ride.

## 21st-Century Timber Production

Timber may no longer be the nationally strategic commodity whose dearth was the decisive factor in stimulating the decision to create the Forestry Commission a century ago, but its production remains a defining purpose of British forestry. Although pit-props and trench boards may be things of the past, the precision output of today's highly automated sawmills is vital to the construction industry, and other advanced facilities producing panels and particle board, or generating green biomass energy, are also dependent on a reliable, high quality output from British forests. The UK is now the world's second largest net importer of forest products (after China), and this strengthening demand means there is a robust market for everything which forests both private and public can sustainably produce.

The importance of timber as a raw material and its relevance to people's everyday lives has in no way been diminished over a century. Its qualities as a renewable and versatile natural resource are increasingly understood whereas materials such as plastics and concrete are increasingly questioned for their lack of sustainability, their polluting qualities or their embedded energy. It is now better understood that growing timber offers a critical additional benefit of absorbing carbon dioxide from the atmosphere, acting as a sink to the carbon emissions driving climate change. Forestry is the only productive land use of which this is true.

Income from timber continues to be the largest single component in the finances of the Forestry Commission, providing approximately half of its total funding, and the work of growing, planting, protecting, harvesting and marketing this crop is the main business of a large part of the workforce, even if it is far less labour intensive than in the past. In England today, for example, the Commission directly operates just four timber harvesters and four forwarders in Kielder Forest and one timber harvester and two forwarders in Thetford Forest – although other machines are operated by harvesting contractors, often on long-term arrangements. Depending on tree size, each harvester fells between 30,000 and 55,000 cubic metres of timber per year, undertaking the work that would at one time have required 30 or more chainsaw operators to do, all with a level of precision, efficiency and operator safety and welfare that could not have been imagined 50 years ago. Forwarders likewise are each extracting between 25,000 and 35,000 cubic metres per year and undertaking work that would have required at least 30 horses and their handlers.

The last century may have proved the economic viability of softwood forestry in Britain but in contrast the management of British broadleaved forests has struggled. Significant areas remain unmanaged or under-managed and British hardwood timber production is barely 1 per cent of the softwood volume handled by British sawmills. The area under broadleaf woodland in England may have increased by over 50 per cent since the 1940s, but for many reasons, including the devastating presence of grey squirrels and limited markets for thinnings, it has proved difficult to build an economic model to support the growing of quality hardwoods. In recent decades the thriving market for biomass and firewood for domestic consumption has provided exciting new outlets for poor quality material allowing improvement of woods. The Commission is an active supplier to these markets, and is also heavily engaged with others in the sector in efforts to bring the large areas of unmanaged broadleaved woodland back into production.

*Picking cones from the top of a Serbian spruce using support pole on top of a ladder lashed to tree. Hampshire, 1963*

The place of timber production in the future of British forests is certain, and the main pressures at work in the contemporary economy are likely to drive increased woodland planting to boost the timber harvests of the second half of the century. There are real challenges. The impact of the steep decline in new planting since the 1980s will inevitably be felt in a decline in timber production in the 2030s and 2040s, even though producers including the Commission will make efforts for both commercial and public policy reasons to smooth out the production profile as far as possible. Modern standards and principles of forest design also mean that the previous productive capacity of many commercial forests will not be equalled on the current rotation, as restocking is carried out at lower overall densities with greater allowance for environmental good practice such as provision of open space, protection of habitats and archaeological features, softening of margins, and special treatment of riparian corridors. The necessity to respond to climate change by implementing bold programmes of forest resilience will also mean that the sawmills of the future will need to adapt to serve their customers' needs with an ever wider variety of species.

The 21st century, in timber production as in other walks of life, will see significant changes, requiring imaginative responses and an ever greater range of human skills and new scientific and technological developments to sustain and grow the practice of professional forestry from the solid foundations laid by the Commission in the 20th.

## Public Support for Forestry

In 2010, the new coalition government faced the pressures of the global financial crisis and resulting austerity. It needed to find ways to raise capital to get the country's finances onto firmer ground, and the public forest estate's attractive asset value of £2 billion led the government to embark on a public consultation exploring different ways in which public forests could be owned and managed in England.

The response from the public was swift and widespread, landing overwhelmingly in support of forests remaining in public hands. Protest was vociferous, both at local and national level, in traditional ways and in the emerging online channels. It was a clear reminder of the powerful connection people have with the forests and woodlands of England.

The public consultation was abandoned, and the government appointed an independent panel led by The Right Reverend James Jones, the Bishop of Liverpool, to review forestry in England. Based on a vast body of evidence, the panel made a range of recommendations which were accepted by the government, and gave a ringing endorsement to the multidimensional value of forests and forestry. 'Our forests and woods', the panel wrote, 'are nature's playground for the adventurous, museum for the curious, hospital for the stressed, cathedral for the spiritual, and a livelihood for the entrepreneur.'

Ultimately, this journey unified support for the Forestry Commission between the forestry industry, the public and the government, resulting in an organisation better prepared for challenges the future may bring. It has now been the firm policy of successive governments, with support from across the political spectrum, to provide strong support for our trees and woodlands, and to keep the public forest estate in trust for the nation.

## Devolution

The end of the 20th century saw one of the most momentous changes in the life of the Commission. Devolution came to forestry in April 1999, the first step in a process which divided responsibility for forestry in Great Britain among the three countries of Scotland, England and Wales. This process ran its course over 20 years, and reached its conclusion in the centenary year.

The Scotland Act 1998 and the Government of Wales Act 1998 transferred the land and property managed by the Commission in Scotland and Wales to Scottish Ministers and the National Assembly for Wales respectively, along with ministerial responsibilities for forestry in the two countries. Separate arrangements have applied in Northern Ireland since 1922. At first this change mainly affected forestry strategies, which began to be written separately for each country, and the institutions of the Commission itself remained largely untouched. The public forests, for example, continued to be managed as a single estate by a unified agency, Forest Enterprise.

The die had been cast, however, and change began to gather pace. A Forestry Devolution Review chaired by the Cabinet Office in 2002 recognised that the landscape had shifted and led to the devolution of key parts of the Commission itself. The estate was divided at the borders, and Forestry Commission England, Forestry Commission Scotland and Forestry Commission Wales were born. The responsibilities once exercised by the Forestry Commissioners across Great Britain were largely delegated to separate National Committees for each country, and inevitably both forestry policies and approaches to management began to diverge.

The shared identity of the Commission remained strong right through the first decade of the 21st century. Although the days when

*Senior forest worker using felling axe for removal of pole-sized stems to achieve general thinning of canopy. Hampshire, 1959*

a member of staff might be posted at short notice from the north of Scotland to the south of England or west Wales were gone, there was still a significant degree of movement from one job to another right across the Commission, and everyone still wore the 'two trees' with pride on their Forestry Commission uniforms. But it was only a matter of time before the irresistible forces of devolution would cut those ties too. In April 2013 Forestry Commission Wales, the Countryside Council for Wales and Environment Agency Wales were combined into a new body – Natural Resources Wales. This took Wales and its forests and forestry out of the Commission altogether, a moment of pride for Wales but also a time of real sadness for those who had to set aside an identity which had become an important part of their lives.

Finally, in April 2019, following the passage of the Forestry and Land Management (Scotland) Act in the Scottish Parliament in 2018, Scotland left the Forestry Commission. The public forests in Scotland – known as the National Forest Estate – passed into the care of a new agency, Forestry and Land Scotland, while responsibility for implementing the Scottish Government's forestry policy passed to a separate agency, Scottish Forestry. This completed the process of devolution, and led to the end of the Forestry Commission's shared GB headquarters in Edinburgh.

The Forestry Commission continues to thrive in England, and the spirit of cooperation between the three countries, strengthened by their shared forestry heritage, remains alive and well. Some specialist areas of work are still done once for all three countries, and perhaps most importantly Forest Research continues, by agreement with the three governments, to carry out its vital applied research work right across our islands. There are even some small areas of deep forest, virtually inaccessible from the 'right' side of the border, which one country or another still cares for and harvests on behalf of its neighbour!

Devolution has changed none of the fundamental issues. The last century has if anything reinforced the value of the forests that were created as a consequence of the 1919 Forestry Act and the truth of the vision of those that created them. Even after devolution the Forestry Commission remains the biggest timber producer and largest landowner in England and Forestry and Land Scotland the biggest timber supplier and landowner in Britain, both by a very significant margin. Modern sustainable forestry, pioneered by the Forestry Commission and still led by the Commission and its successor bodies, lies at the heart of an efficient and world class multi-billion-pound timber and wood processing industry which supports tens of thousands of jobs. All year round, British forests produce timber, support wildlife, and are visited by millions of people. This is a good place from which to take on the challenge of the next hundred years.

# PART TWO: AMONG THE TREES

## CHAPTER I

# Silviculture

---

The word 'silviculture' may be unfamiliar but it is simply the theory and practice of establishing and maintaining communities of trees and other woody vegetation that have value for people and society. A forester controls the density and species composition of a forest by favouring or removing trees and also influences its renewal by ensuring young trees replace those that are harvested. Silviculture includes the creation of new forests by planting young trees on bare land and making sure they survive and grow so that they can form a canopy and shade that out-competes other vegetation. As such, silviculture is the core business of the Forestry Commission.

The species composition and the structure of Britain's original forest or 'wildwood' developed in response to factors such as temperature, rainfall, exposure and browsing mammals that, as we will see later, modern forestry has had to quantify and understand. These native woodlands were largely cleared for agriculture during the last millennium so that much timber was imported from Europe and North America. The consequent lack of domestic timber supplies during the First World War and the need to replenish British forests gave rise to the formation of the Forestry Commission. In the broadleaved forests that survived clearance, a specific type of silviculture was applied that took advantage of the ability of broadleaved species to grow again after the tree has been felled. This type of silviculture, known as 'coppicing', has been carried out for millennia, starting in the Neolithic period, and has had a profound effect on our native broadleaved woodlands.

The publication in 1664 of John Evelyn's *Sylva, or A Discourse of Forest-Trees and the Propagation of Timber* was the start of many changes in silviculture in Britain. The book was a call to plant more trees and protect the Royal forests for the production of oak timber for shipbuilding by the Royal Navy. As with coppicing, the ethos of growing oak for shipbuilding has left an important mark on our broadleaved woodlands. Evelyn also advocated carrying out inventories to ensure that there were future supplies and encouraged use of the latest forest management techniques. In subsequent decades a number of private estates began to innovate with silvicultural practice and the forests they created were a foretaste of forestry in the modern era. The most notable example of this was in Perthshire, Scotland where the second Duke of Atholl imported large quantities of larch seed from the Alps in the 18th century to create new plantation forests on moorland.

During the Victorian era, there were three main developments in British silviculture: the influence of continental practice, increasing use of conifers, and the creation of new plantation forests on bare ground. Countries such as Germany and France had applied themselves to the management of their forests over several centuries and were an obvious source of information and inspiration. The Forest Service in India, formed in 1855 some 64 years before the Forestry Commission, had made use of continental expertise and notable Germans such as Dietrich Brandis and William Schlich worked in senior positions in the Indian Forest Service before returning to work in Britain. The publication of *Schlich's Manual of Forestry*, published in five volumes between 1889 and 1896, resulted in the wider use of conifers and plantations. However, the application of these developments was limited because the area of forest was still very low (5 per cent in 1900) and many forests lacked a systematic approach to management. These factors, alongside the effects of the First World War, were fundamental to the formation of the Forestry Commission.

With its mild oceanic climate, fertile soils and plentiful rainfall, Britain really is a fantastic place to grow trees. Many other parts of the world that span the same latitudinal range as mainland Britain (50–59°N) have forests that are much less productive of timber. The main reason for this is the North Atlantic Drift, an ocean current that keeps Britain warmer and wetter than places in continental Europe. For example, the average annual temperatures for Edinburgh, Vilnius and Moscow, which are all at latitude of 55°N, are 9.1°C, 5.6°C and 4.4°C respectively. In terms of growth conditions for trees these apparently minor differences in temperature are very significant.

Any tree requires sunlight, oxygen, carbon dioxide, water, suitable temperatures and soils (to provide nutrients and anchorage) for adequate growth. All of these factors are important and can be influenced by others such as exposure and aspect. However, water, temperature and soils have direct and significant effects on the species composition of a forest or the species that can be planted to form a new forest. For example, wet soils and areas around watercourses favour willows, poplars and alder; light, sandy soils favour birch; oak is found on both dry and saturated soils. In more exposed aspects, pines, with their thin needle-like leaves, are better able to cope with the effects of wind than broadleaves. In the original wildwood, pine forests occupied colder, less fertile sites in northern Scotland, while in the warmer, drier south, lime, oak, hazel and elm were dominant. The Forestry Commission's Ecological Site Classification (ESC) has been developed to take account of the main ecological factors affecting growth and to help foresters select tree species for the current and future climate. It defines seven climate zones and a recent analysis of the public forest estate after 100 years has shown that of the 20 most commonly planted tree species, 17 are grown in the warm-dry zone, 15 in the warm-moist zone but only seven in the cold-wet zone. Species choice is much more limited in colder regions.

In the early years of the Forestry Commission many of the basic facts of silviculture, including how growth would be affected by the factors described above, were poorly understood. One of the Commission's earliest and most famous experiments took place in Beddgelert Forest in north Wales. Its objective was to study the influence of exposure on different species. The experimental area was divided into 25 plots with five rows across the slope and five columns running up and down the slope (from about 410 to 560 metres above sea level). Five treatments were selected for testing: two species were planted pure (Sitka spruce and Japanese larch) and three were 50:50 mixtures of two species (Sitka spruce–Japanese larch, Sitka spruce–lodgepole pine, Norway spruce–European larch). To allow scientific comparison of the five treatments, each is represented once in each row and column. This type of experiment is known as a Latin square and was a scientific breakthrough when it was developed in the 1920s by the eminent statistician Sir Ronald Fisher at Rothamsted Experiment Station in Hertfordshire. The experiment at Beddgelert is historically important because it is the first field experiment anywhere in the world to use one of Fisher's randomised designs.

It is clear from the history of the experiment that at the beginning Forestry Commission scientists did not fully understand how exposure would affect tree growth, in some cases believing that lower plots would be more exposed than higher ones. Instead, the experiment showed that, as elevation increased, the productivity of all the treatments declines, and there is an effect across the slope in terms of the growth of trees. Of the five treatments, one mixture (Norway spruce–European larch) was unsuccessful because both of the species were unsuited to such a high-elevation, exposed site. The other four treatments were a success but data from the experiment show that, whether planted pure or in mixture, the volume production of Sitka spruce was far superior to either Japanese larch or lodgepole pine. The other interesting aspect of the experiment was the selection of the treatments. It seems clear that one of the aims of the experiment was to verify the promise of Sitka spruce and Japanese larch. However, as three of the treatments were mixtures of two different species, it is clear that, at this early stage in the development of the Forestry Commission, the culture of planting pure stands of one species was not the accepted norm that it would become in future years.

When concerned with growing trees, an important part of any forester's job is to measure what has been produced. Although timber is only one of a huge variety of different benefits produced by a forest, it is a key requirement for professional management of forests that current and future timber production are quantified. Foresters measure the diameter of a tree – the convention is to do this at 1.3 metres above ground, known as 'breast height' – as well as its full height. Converting these measurements into volume is complicated by the fact that the shapes of different species of tree are not alike and are also affected by the growing conditions of the tree. For example, an oak tree grown in the open will have a different stem shape to one in a plantation. One of the very significant achievements of the Forestry Commission has been the development of a system whereby the volume growth of a stand of trees can be assessed using a small number of height measurements combined with the age of the stand. This is known as the Yield Class (YC) system: for example, a stand assessed to be YC8 will produce a mean annual

Nootka cypress *(Xanthocyparis nootkatensis)*

volume increment of 8 cubic metres per hectare at its maximum growth rate.

In broad terms there are two options for species choice – pure or mixed-species (both options were used at Beddgelert) – and two options for the structure of the forest – uniform or irregular. In a uniform forest all the trees are planted or regenerated at the same time; once established the trees grow together and compete for resources. Thinning can be used to manage the density of trees until they are felled. In a forest with an irregular structure, trees of different sizes exist within the same management unit and trees of the same age are usually present in groups of different sizes. Uniform forests are used to grow timber and produce trees with a small range of diameters at a known point of time in the future when they are clear-felled (clear-felling involves cutting down all trees on an area of forest greater than a quarter of a hectare). They can also serve a range of other environmental and social objectives; for example, large areas of uniform stands of mixed broadleaved species were planted in Britain after 1985 as part of the effort to increase the area of forest composed of native species. Uniform forests regenerated using clear-felling can also produce the open habitat required for specific flora and fauna; for example, for nightjars and woodlarks in Thetford Forest. Forests with an irregular structure, where only individual trees or small groups are felled, are a good way of managing forests where the maintenance of a forest canopy is important, for example on slopes to reduce soil erosion or to reduce the negative landscape impacts of clear-felling, and combining this with timber production (an approach also known as 'continuous cover forestry'). Of the four main silvicultural options, one of these, uniform stands of pure species, has been the main option employed by the Forestry Commission. However, to meet future challenges, a more balanced approach between the four options will need to be adopted.

The first 100 years of the Forestry Commission have seen dramatic changes in the objectives set for our forests. Today these objectives include a full range of social, environmental and economic objectives delivered using sustainable forest management. However, when the Commission was set up it was tasked with building up a strategic reserve of timber by creating a State forest enterprise to expand forest cover. Although these early plantations – large expanses of new forests composed of non-native conifers mainly in the uplands of Britain – have come to symbolise the Forestry Commission, today's planting is far more diverse – a mixture of broadleaf and conifer that is far better able to deliver the multiple aims of the modern Commission.

# The Species of the Forests

Looking at a map of forest cover of Great Britain, it is clear that conifers – mainly of non-native species – are most prominent in the north and west of Britain whereas broadleaves – mainly of native species – are generally dominant in the south and east of the country. Today, the dominant species for silviculture in Britain is Sitka spruce, a vigorous and productive tree from coastal areas in the Pacific Northwest of North America, which has been shown to grow well on infertile soils with harsh climatic conditions. It is these soils and conditions that have provided the main opportunities for forest expansion in Britain.

Following the retreat of the glaciers and the formation of the English Channel, Britain was left with a limited number of native tree species, generally regarded to include three conifers (Scots pine, juniper and yew) and 32 broadleaves. The history of introduced species to Britain is a long one which probably goes back to the beginnings of recorded history and certainly gained momentum from the 16th century onwards. Many of the introduced species were imported to be specimen trees in parks and gardens; they were brought in by those wealthy enough to fund expeditions to find new species and to provide suitable settings in which these species could be planted and cared for. Alan Mitchell, in his much-respected book *A Field Guide to the Trees of Britain and Northern Europe* (1974), lists 134 collections of trees in Britain and Ireland where the results of many of these plantings are still available for us to study and enjoy. There are many more. Much of this rich heritage was made possible by a long succession of eminent plant collectors such as David Douglas and Ernest Wilson, who brought to our attention trees from many remote areas of the world. This activity included the introduction of Norway spruce, sycamore and sweet chestnut before the 16th century and European larch in about 1620 up to the main period for introductions in the 19th century, which included Douglas fir in 1827 and Sitka spruce in 1831.

It was probably not until about the beginning of the 18th century that conifers were planted as a forest with the aim of producing timber rather than being planted as ornamental trees, and the first species was the native Scots pine. An early innovator was the Earl of Haddington who described the methods he developed for planting forests, including Scots pine (which he called Scotch fir), in his *A Short Treatise on Forest-Trees: Aquaticks, Ever-Greens, Fences and Grass-Seeds* (1756), methods that most modern foresters would recognise as notch planting, still widely used today.

> I make one to go with a spade, who strikes it into the ground, presses it backwards and forwards till the slit is made wide enough to receive the root, which the man with the basket sets in, and then with his foot presses the slit together.

In subsequent years Scots pine was widely planted throughout Britain but there were concerns about its slow rate of growth and inability to grow on some sites. As a result, there was increasing interest in European larch. An interesting point is that Norway spruce, an earlier introduction and a better volume producer then either Scots pine or European larch, was, until the 20th century, relatively unimportant. Much of our early silvicultural knowledge of European larch, such as its sensitivity to exposure and soil requirements, arose from its widespread use on the Atholl Estates near Pitlochry in Scotland. Interest in larch was also sustained by the introduction in 1861 of Japanese larch. At this stage the European larch was suffering badly from larch canker and the new introduction was eventually shown to be more resistant to this pathogen and able to grow on wetter, more exposed sites than the European species.

At the end of the 19th century the introduction of tree species for both ornamental purposes and for forestry led to a massive increase in our knowledge of trees. To try to capture this knowledge, Henry John Elwes and Augustine Henry published *The Trees of Great Britain and Ireland* in six volumes between 1906 and 1913, the objective of which was to 'give a complete account of all the trees which grow naturally or are cultivated in Great Britain, and which have attained, or seem likely to attain a size which justifies their being looked on as timber trees'. The main driver for the authors to compile this information was that

> Forestry is at last making headway as a science in this country, but too many of the books recently published on the subject have been based on continental experience, which is not directly applicable to the very different conditions of climate, soil, labour and market existing here.

Not surprisingly, given that Great Britain has so few native tree species, this seminal work featured many non-native species. As William Turner Thiselton-Dyer, a leading British botanist and the third director of the Royal Botanic Gardens, Kew, states in his preface: 'The United Kingdom offers a hospitality to exotic vegetation which finds no parallel in the Northern temperate region of the globe.'

Six years after the publication of the last volume of Elwes and Henry's series, the Forestry Commission was formed and its early leaders recognised their advice that science must play a central role in the choice of species and designing a silviculture appropriate to Britain. In the following years the Commission developed a useful three-stage process for any new species to pass through before it could be accepted for widespread use in the forest. In the first stage it was planted as a specimen tree in gardens, arboreta and parks to distinguish those that were unsuited to the climate from those that could survive or, better still, thrive and demonstrate potential. The second stage was to trial the promising species in experimental plots or small plantations covering a range of soil and climate conditions as a test of whether it had the potential to become a forest tree capable of producing useful timber. The third stage was to trial the successful species from earlier stages as plantation species in a limited way, including some more testing sites, to get a fair measure of the true potential of the species if it were used more widely.

At its formation in 1919 the Forestry Commission was keen to undertake trialling a range of different species as part of the first stage of species selection. At this time the Royal Botanic Gardens, Kew was also seeking a new site to replace its conifer collection, which was thought to be rapidly deteriorating through the combined adverse effects of poor soil and increasing atmospheric pollution. Following a number of informal conversations, in 1922 Roy Robinson of the Forestry Commission made a formal proposal to establish a new pinetum to Arthur Hill, then director at Kew:

> I understand indirectly that you have been considering the desirability of finding a site for an arboretum away from Kew, which is unsuitable for many coniferous species. Perhaps we could help in this respect, as we now have estates all over the country and could spare the relatively small area which would be required for the purpose.

These actions led to the formation of the pinetum at Bedgebury in Kent. This site and the other national tree collections at Westonbirt (Gloucestershire), Brechfa (Carmarthenshire), Lynford (Norfolk) and Kilmun (Argyll and Bute), along with numerous regional collections, each of which has a fascinating history, have made a significant contribution to our knowledge of how a vast range of tree species grows on the varied soils and climate throughout Britain.

The second stage of the species selection process has been one of the main achievements of research carried out by the Forestry Commission. The approach has been based strongly on field experimentation which has generally used scientific methods similar to those in the Beddgelert Forest experiment described earlier. Throughout its history a hallmark of the Commission has been the rapidity with which research findings have been transferred to field practice: promising species from the second stage of species trialling were quickly adopted and, on an appropriate scale, used more widely as a plantation species, the third stage of species selection.

The Commission's trialling of over 160 taxa of non-native species in a monograph *Exotic Forest Trees in Great Britain* was reviewed by James MacDonald et al. in 1957 and presented to the seventh British Commonwealth Forestry Conference held in Australia and New Zealand. However, at the same time as MacDonald was presenting his paper, the Zuckerman Report was published, heralding the start of the economic era in British forestry. The main effect of this change in policy was that it snuffed out interest in a wide range of potential plantation species and focused attention on one species, Sitka spruce.

It is interesting to note that over the first 100 years of the Forestry Commission the range of species planted has not changed much: the eight conifer species that were most commonly planted in 1921–30 (Scots pine, Corsican pine, lodgepole pine, Sitka spruce, Norway spruce, European larch, Japanese larch, Douglas fir) are the same as those planted in more recent times. However, there have been dramatic changes in the proportions of the species planted; the most outstanding example is the increased use of Sitka spruce and the decrease in the planting of Scots pine. During the 1970s, 63 per cent of all conifer forests planted in Britain were composed of Sitka spruce. The duration and intensity of this rise to dominance has been such that by 2003 29 per cent of all forests in Britain were composed of Sitka spruce.

There are two main reasons why Sitka spruce has been so dominant in the development of the Forestry Commission and the forests of Britain. Firstly, botanically it is an excellent species choice for the type of land that was available for creating forests. These were generally in the uplands and had wet, infertile soils and harsh climatic conditions. Research had confirmed that Sitka spruce was well suited to grow in such environments and could produce more volume than many other species as well as a readily marketable timber. Secondly, in the economic era of forestry, analysis showed that Sitka spruce, even when growing on a suboptimal site, was economically superior to other species in terms of ease of establishment, growth rates and volume of timber.

# Conifers and Forest Expansion

Agricultural policy in the early years of the Forestry Commission dictated that better quality land could not be converted to forestry, so inevitably the process of expansion was concentrated upon areas of marginal agricultural ground in the uplands of Britain. The upland zone in Britain has been defined in a variety of ways but a widespread definition is that it comprises land lying above areas enclosed for agriculture, generally at more than 250 metres above sea level. About one-third of the surface area of Britain is upland, including substantial areas of the Scottish

Highlands and Scottish Borders, the Pennines, the Lake District, the North York Moors, the Welsh Mountains, and Dartmoor and Exmoor.

At the beginning of the 20th century, many parts of the upland zone had limited natural tree cover, and were often used for hill grazing or for sporting purposes such as grouse moors or deer stalking. In the eastern parts of the upland zone, vegetation was dominated by heathers and associated species, and by various grasses (e.g. purple moor grass, deer grass, cotton grass), often accompanied by mosses in more westerly regions. Typically, soils were poor in nutrients, and were often characterised by a layer of peat overlying the mineral layers. The mineral soil might be gleyed (caused by waterlogging) as in extensive parts of Kielder Forest in Northumberland; it might contain an iron pan (a hard layer of mainly iron oxides) as in areas in the North York Moors; or the depth of peat could be 1 metre or more as in the Flow Country of Sutherland and Caithness in northern Scotland. A feature of upland soils like these was that they were not free-draining and, without cultivation, presented an appreciable barrier to the root development of young trees. The rolling topography characteristic of many upland zones (e.g. the Scottish Borders) plus the lack of existing tree cover meant that there was little shelter available for young trees, and wind exposure would prove to be an important feature in the development of the new forests.

Attempts had been made to establish plantations in the uplands for at least a century before the foundation of the Forestry Commission. There were some notable successes, such as the establishment of the Atholl larch plantations mentioned earlier, but there were also many failures. Even when trees were established, growth rates were often slow and productivity was poor. Neither was conducive to the prime objective of creating a strategic timber reserve.

Probably the most important afforestation project in upland Britain before the foundation of the Forestry Commission was that begun in 1892 on the Corrour Estate in the central Highlands of Scotland. Here, working at elevations of around 400 metres on acid, peaty soils and largely treeless sites, John Stirling Maxwell and his foresters adapted techniques previously developed in Belgium to show that three measures were necessary to establish young trees under testing upland conditions in Britain: cutting drains to remove surface water; planting trees on upturned turves which provided freedom from competing vegetation;

and using phosphate fertiliser to promote good early growth. Provided these measures were used, it was possible to establish healthy stands of Sitka spruce on infertile soils – stands that gave a better yield than Scots pine, the other major conifer trialled at Corrour. By the time of Maxwell's death in 1956, these techniques had been used to establish nearly 300 hectares of forest at Corrour with extensive areas of Sitka spruce and natural regeneration of this non-native species was first recorded there in the 1940s. The pioneering nature of his work was recognised and studied by many people who were influential in the early development of the Forestry Commission, including Roy Robinson (Chairman, 1932–52), who wrote to Maxwell immediately after the Second World War: 'I regard your pioneer work there [at Corrour] as the most valuable ever done in Britain and an inspiration to the subsequent developments which we have brought about.'

Despite the successful establishment of trees at Corrour, there was still initial uncertainty as to how far 'up the hill' tree planting could be extended in different part of Britain as shown by this extract from A. L. Hopkinson's original (1926) acquisition report for Kielder Forest in northern England.

> The area [the North Tyne Valley of what is now Kielder Forest] will prove a difficult one from two points of view. Firstly, in acquisition and management, ... the actual plantable land may be costly ... because of the necessities of taking over considerable areas of unplantable land ... Secondly, the whole technique of the afforestation of such land bristles with difficulties and calls for intensive supervision and foresters of considerably greater intelligence than are normally found in the Commission's service.

Therefore, from the 1920s onwards, the field foresters and research staff of the Forestry Commission spent considerable efforts in trying to improve the techniques trialled at Corrour to support an extensive programme of upland afforestation. This involved detailed applied research into aspects of planting stock production in nurseries, methods of site cultivation and drainage, and techniques for vegetation management and for remedial fertilisation. Comprehensive summaries of the key results from the experimental work were provided in two classic Forestry Commission

*Bulletins* written by John Zehetmayr in 1954 and 1960 dealing with the afforestation of peats and upland heaths respectively. Much of this work was carried out in experimental reserves (forests) located in different parts of the countries where the results of the latest trials could be demonstrated to field foresters and also communicated to senior staff who took an active interest in this work. One of the most famous reserves was on the Lon Mor (the 'big waste'), near Fort Augustus in north Scotland. Here, in the late 1940s, a disagreement about the best establishment practice between four senior staff of the Commission (the then Chairman, Director-General, Chief Research Officer, and Regional Director) resulted in four different plots being laid out to find who was correct. One of these senior people (unfortunately the records do not say which) was later found to have damaged the trees in plots belonging to his competitors!

By the 1930s, the results from these experiments supported the findings from Corrour and gave field staff the confidence to purchase large tracts of land in the uplands for the creation of new forests. Initially it had been thought that perhaps no more than one-third of the total area acquired at Kielder would be suitable for establishing forests. In 1995, however, the then Kielder Forest District Manager Bob McIntosh reported that the developments in afforestation techniques that had been achieved through the period 1925–60 had allowed nearly 70 per cent of the area to be successfully planted. These developments included the increasing use of wheeled and caterpillar tractors to mechanise site cultivation and drainage, the application of chemical herbicides to control ground vegetation, and site classification systems which could be linked with fertiliser prescriptions to remove limiting factors to tree growth.

The mastery of afforestation techniques that had been developed during the first 50 years of the Forestry Commission gave staff the confidence that forests could be successfully established on many parts of the uplands that had not carried tree cover for several centuries. In the 1980s, John Davies, the senior Forestry Commission manager in southern Scotland, reviewed the standard silviculture used in the establishment and management of Sitka spruce plantations, taking the view that the forester 'has a remarkable dominion over the site, except for the climate'.

As part of the expansion of forestry after the Second World

War, foresters began to wonder where the exact limits to biological and economic tree growth in the British uplands might lie. Due to deforestation, there were few natural tree lines to give guidance as to the precise elevations where trees might or might not grow. There were extensive areas of marginal agricultural land on poor peat soils in northern Scotland which had been considered unplantable before the war. In the 1950s and 1960s a series of trial plantations was planted at high elevations (up to 600 metres across upland Britain or in very exposed sites such as the Outer Hebrides and the Northern Isles) to try to ascertain the potential limits to tree growth. All sites were established using the best afforestation techniques (e.g. soil drainage and cultivation, fertiliser inputs) and a small range of exposure-tolerant species were planted. During the same period a brilliantly simple and robust method of characterising wind exposure using 'tatter flags' was developed (see Chapter 4, p. 168). The results of these trials and from the tatter flag network showed that most sites could be successfully planted using modern afforestation techniques, that lodgepole pine and Sitka spruce had the most satisfactory growth, and that wind exposure was the factor which most severely limited tree growth.

Awareness of the potential negative impacts of wind on upland forests was to increase during the second half of the 20th century. The first thinnings of closed canopy stands in the newly planted upland forests (for example at Kielder) started in the late 1940s and early 1950s and foresters were dismayed to find that the opening up of the stands was often followed by wind-blow. This problem became more widespread as thinning occurred in other maturing forests. There was also the severe damage caused by major storms such as those of 1953 and 1968. Further experience suggested that windthrow (the overturning of trees in strong winds) could prove to be endemic on shallow rooting soils with little topographic shelter from winter gales. During the 1960s and 1970s, extensive research was undertaken to try to understand the various processes that influenced the occurrence of windthrow, which resulted in the development of the Windthrow Hazard Classification in the late 1970s. This predicted the occurrence of windthrow on a given site as a function of location, elevation, topographic shelter and soil type. It was also found that, if delayed beyond a certain age (tree height), thinning could considerably increase the risk of windthrow. As a result, on more exposed sites (i.e. higher windthrow hazard classes), many stands were not thinned, with felling taking place at a younger age. This method of classifying the likelihood of windthrow was widely applied throughout the forestry sector, and was seen internationally as a pioneer in systems seeking to classify the risks to forests from a climatic agent. More recent developments have seen the system refined into a windthrow risk model (ForestGALES) which predicts the probable occurrence of windthrow, and calculates the risk of damage upon different stand structures.

Because of the importance of the wind climate, nearly all stands in upland forests were managed under a clear-felling regime with all the trees being felled at a comparatively young age. Perhaps the only concessions to 'non-market' aspects of forest management were to seek to modify the shapes and sizes of felled areas to minimise visual impacts and to stagger felling ages of adjacent stands so that greater age and size variation was introduced across a landscape. This simple silvicultural approach overlooked the wide range of variation in upland forest soils and sites which offered the possibility of growing other species such as Douglas fir, redwoods and silver firs, and developing mixed species stands of a range of sizes which would be more visually attractive and could offer greater resilience to the impacts of climate change. This alternative approach to forest management is often termed Continuous Cover Forestry (CCF) and since 2000 has been introduced on a trial basis in a number of Commission forests throughout Britain. These trials build on some attempts in the 1950s to increase species and structural diversity in planted forests in Scotland, most of which were instigated by Mark Anderson, then professor of forestry at Edinburgh University but previously one of the Commission's first researchers.

The expansion of planted forests (largely composed of non-native conifers) across large areas of upland Britain was probably the major land-use change that occurred in Britain in the 20th century. Although the expansion of forests in the last two decades of that century was primarily due to the activity of private-sector foresters, the silvicultural methods used and the species planted by private foresters were essentially those pioneered by the Forestry Commission in previous decades. Forests created in places such as Ae (Dumfries and Galloway), Clocaenog (north-east Wales), Fernworthy (Dartmoor), Glentrool (Galloway), Hamsterley (near Durham), Kielder (Northumberland), Radnor (central

Wales) and Wykeham (near Scarborough) demonstrated potential for growth that would encourage and stimulate the expansion of private forestry across upland Britain.

As well as the expansion of conifer forests across upland Britain, the Forestry Commission had to consider how best to approach the management of the native pinewoods of northern Scotland. This oceanic outlier of the northern boreal forests used to cover extensive areas of the Scottish Highlands but conversion to agriculture, overgrazing and unsustainable harvesting had massively reduced the extent of these forests by the beginning of the 20th century. Many remaining trees of good timber quality in these woods were felled during the two world wars with the result that the surviving forests were generally understocked and with low numbers of young trees. By 1950, the Commission had acquired a number of the larger remnant pinewoods such as Glen More, Glen Affric and the Black Wood of Rannoch and local foresters were faced with the challenge of how best to restore these damaged woodlands to a healthier state. Early research trials had shown the difficulty of achieving successful natural regeneration, partly because of high deer populations, and sometimes it seemed simpler to plant up the open areas in the pinewoods with non-native species like Sitka spruce. However, in 1959 the publication of a now classic book, *The Native Pinewoods of Scotland*, by Jock Carlisle and Professor H. M. Steven (previously one of the Commission's first Research Officers) brought the importance of these pinewoods to a wider audience, leading to a gradual acceptance that they constituted an ecosystem worth conserving in its own right. As a consequence, maintenance and expansion of the native pinewoods have now become an aspiration of Scottish forestry policy. Local foresters, such as Finlay Macrae in Glen Affric, carried out early trials which showed how to encourage regeneration in areas where deer numbers were controlled through fencing and culling. Building on this pioneering work, in the 1990s Forestry Commission staff embarked on a programme of restoring all the native pinewoods in public ownership to a favourable condition through removal of non-native tree species, encouragement of natural regeneration, and rigorous control of deer numbers. This approach has also been used in pinewoods owned by NGOs such as the RSPB and is encouraged in privately owned pinewoods through forestry grants.

Many of the main achievements in silviculture in Great Britain have been based on scientific research carried out by the Forestry Commission. A good example of this is the work undertaken on genetic variation within introduced conifer species which has refined their use and led to improvements in productivity and timber quality. For example, the natural range of Sitka spruce in the Pacific Northwest is roughly 3,000 kilometres in length from Kodiak Island, Alaska to Mendocino County, California and the only way to define where best to collect seed for the best growth in Britain has been through scientific research. Seed collected from throughout this range will not grow uniformly when planted out in Britain – more northerly seed origins will grow more slowly. A more recent benefit of research has been the widescale use of improved planting material with gains of up to 25 per cent in volume productivity.

# The Story of Broadleaved Woodlands

In the history of the Forestry Commission, conifers have dominated. However, the story of the development of broadleaved silviculture is worth telling because it shows some of the very best aspects of the Commission and its ability to learn from mistakes.

Conifers can generally grow two or three times faster than broadleaved species, hence their employment in the early years of the Commission when establishing the timber reserve was the primary focus. In the late 1930s, after nearly 20 years of the strategic reserve policy, there was some public criticism of its conifer tree planting programmes. In response to these comments and in an early recognition of the importance of broadleaved woodland, the Commission offered Eustace Jones of the University of Oxford Forestry Department the opportunity to set up an ecological reserve in a broadleaved woodland: Lady Park Wood, situated in the gorge of the river Wye in Monmouthshire, was established in 1944. In an attempt to observe and understand the character of natural woodland, it was agreed that there would be no interventions in the reserve. The majority of the area had been untouched since 1920 and was dominated by beech, oak, ash, elm, lime, birch, cherry and alder trees dating back to the 19th century.

At the start of the project it was believed that the reserve was returning to a primeval, natural condition because there were no silvicultural interventions and only natural processes were operating. Until the 1970s the reserve was not disturbed, the trees grew in size and as a result some died; with reduced access to light, the shrubs in the understorey were eliminated and species diversity reduced. From the 1970s onwards there have been some significant changes: Dutch elm disease killed many trees; there was a severe drought in 1976; a heavy spring snowfall in 1983 caused damage; there was a plague of voles in 1985; grey squirrels (which arrived in the area in the 1940s) constantly strip bark from young trees; since the 1980s there has been significant browsing pressure from deer. Throughout this period the reduction in species diversity has continued and in conservation terms the reserve is now rated 'unfavourable, declining'. The original intention of observing and understanding the character of natural woodland by not carrying out any silvicultural interventions has been questioned: it is just not that simple. In fact, what we have learned from studies of Lady Park Wood by ecologist George Peterken is that if we want diverse functioning woodland, for whatever objective, some silvicultural interventions are required even if they are limited to protecting areas of natural regeneration with a fence to prevent deer browsing. However, generally more than just fencing is required. Many authorities now agree that native woodlands are at their most ecologically diverse when canopy cover is well below 100 per cent, as was probably the case in the distant prehistoric past, and was certainly the case historically in wood pastures and managed coppice woodlands; silviculture is the best way to recreate these conditions. In other words, in many situations interventions such as thinning can have a very positive effect on biodiversity.

At about the same time as Lady Park Wood began to be monitored, the Commission was also planning a census of woodlands, the main objective of which was to assess the impact of the Second World War on Britain's woodlands. When the results were published they were 'disheartening': at 6.1 per cent forest cover was still low and 40 per cent of this was classified as unproductive because of heavy wartime felling. Of the total forest approximately 50 per cent was broadleaved forest, 22 per cent was high forest (a type of forest established from seed or planted seedlings), 10 per cent coppice, and 19 per cent was either 'scrub' or 'devastated'. The broadleaved woodlands had borne the brunt of the felling because much of the young conifer forest was not mature enough to yield timber of the required sizes. After the war, silviculture in these broadleaved forests was heavily influenced by the policy of creating a strategic reserve and the desire to increase productivity. As a result conifers were introduced on a large scale to broadleaved woodland. The form of this introduction varied but was mainly of three types: clearance of an unproductive area followed by planting conifers; underplanting low-density broadleaves with suitable conifers; planting conifers, or mixtures of conifers and broadleaved species, when forests were being regenerated. At the height of the economic era, this approach even included applying chemicals to the broadleaves to kill them and favour the conifers. This widespread 'coniferisation' of broadleaved woodland added to the concerns of many stakeholders about the direction of silvicultural practice in Britain.

At this point it is worth recalling the (admittedly modern) definition of silviculture cited earlier: the theory and practice of establishing and maintaining communities of trees and other woody vegetation *that have value for people and society*. We now understand the importance of the last seven words of this definition but in the first 50 years of the Forestry Commission, silviculture was synonymous with maximising timber production, largely ignoring important social and environmental objectives. This trend continued throughout the 1960s and the early-to mid-1970s and a parallel trend was some large-scale clearances of broadleaved woodland for agriculture. These practices were increasingly questioned and eminent forest ecologists such as George Peterken and Oliver Rackham proposed new ways of thinking about the management of our broadleaved woodland (discussed in more detail in Chapter 2).

Eventually, in 1979, concerns about broadleaved woodlands were raised in the House of Lords Select Committee report *Scientific Aspects of Forestry*. This led three years later to the setting-up of a Broadleaves Policy Review Group by the Forestry Commission. As a result, in 1985, a new policy for broadleaved woodlands was announced that aimed to encourage effective and sympathetic management by trying to achieve a balance between different objectives. Clearance and coniferisation of broadleaved woodlands was halted and the special value of ancient semi-natural woodland was recognised (i.e forests on sites that have been continuously wooded since 1600 in England and Wales and 1750 in Scotland). The Forestry Commission emerged from this saga bruised and battered but determined to learn from its mistakes. In the 34 years since 1985 the Commission has shown leadership and authority on many aspects of protecting and enhancing the broadleaved woodland resource of Great Britain. Arguably the main achievements have been enabling an increase of approximately 80 per cent in the area of broadleaved woodland from 1945 to 2010; the development of the tree shelter by Forestry Commission silvicultural researcher Graham Tuley as an aid to planting trees; the publication of authoritative guidance such as *Managing Native Broadleaved Woodland* by R. Harmer et al. (2010). However, these successes need to be set against the context of the ongoing significant problems of mammal damage, predominantly by deer and grey squirrels.

# Silvicultural Challenges for Foresters in 2019

Many of the silvicultural challenges faced by the Forestry Commission in its first 100 years could, possibly, have been foreseen by the people planting the trees in 1919. However, there seems little chance they could have predicted the main ones facing foresters in 2019: the rapid recent rise in pests and diseases, and the challenges of climate change. Recently, trees in Britain have been subjected to a significant increase in the number of new pests and diseases (discussed in more detail in Chapter 4) and many of these have had significant impacts on the main forest species in Britain (in order of coverage: Sitka spruce, Scots pine, oak, birch, lodgepole pine, ash, larch, beech, Norway spruce, sycamore, Corsican pine and Douglas fir). One of the most significant of these diseases is the pathogen *Phytophthora ramorum*, first discovered in the UK on a viburnum plant at a garden centre in Sussex in 2002 and then found to be killing larch trees in a forest in south-west England in 2009. Measures to control it included the felling of 16,000 hectares of larch forests, a huge area equivalent to the whole of Glengarry Forest in Scotland, the tenth largest in Britain. This worrying event has focused attention on the fact that just 12 tree species account for 85 per cent of the forest cover in Britain, another outcome of the economic era of forestry.

The limited diversity of tree species that have hitherto dominated British forestry, both coniferous and broadleaved, whether aimed at timber production or at native woodland restoration, is a significant threat to the resilience of our forests in the future. Just as the loss of larch and the decline of Corsican pine have had a major impact on commercial forestry in some areas of the country, so the loss of elm and the progressive failure of ash have come as heavy blows to many native woodlands. The economic and landscape impact of problems for individual species are amplified if species diversity is limited.

As in so many other areas of life, climate change is forcing us to reconsider our assumptions. In a recent paper, 'Forest Resilience in British Forests, Woods and Plantations – Past and Future Forests in Britain', in the *Quarterly Journal of Forestry*, the Forestry Commission's Jonathan Spencer has challenged us to accept that 'Dramatic changes to the environment within which the next generation of our trees will be maturing thus appear inevitable.' Spencer suggests that

> Increased extremes in the weather have long been predicted, but the science also points out that we can only avert the worst if we act boldly and act soon ... Even if we stop pumping carbon dioxide into the atmosphere and limit global warming to 2°C, a cascade of tipping points may result in a warming of 4 or 5° or more; an environment not seen since the mid Tertiary some 20 million years ago ... For forest managers [the challenges of the coming century] include tree establishment and silviculture having to accommodate conditions not anticipated at all a century ago.

Considering the lessons for resilient 21st century silviculture from the study of past climates and forests in the light of the known facts about current and future climate change must lead to some challenging conclusions. In Spencer's words:

• We ... have either lost, or never had, a suite of trees adapted to the cold wet conditions and gleyed or peaty soils of north-western Europe.

Western hemlock *(Tsuga heterophylla)*

To make our upland and western forests more resilient and maintain their capacity for timber production we will have to look to north-west American forest trees, chosen for their performance as timber, and find European or north-American associates that might impart resilience against changing conditions and novel pests and diseases.

• Longer term changes in our possible climate future may take us towards uncomfortable territory and the need to consider forest species that have long since been lost to Europe as native elements.

• Many of these trees are already present in the modern landscape in parks, gardens and arboreta. These trees will no doubt respond in any event as changing climatic conditions allow for their reproduction and spread across the landscape. We should consider such species on their merits and assess our response accordingly.

... Changes in climate are not new challenges to forests per se; forests in some form will persist and thrive. But they will be forests of species and composition unfamiliar to foresters and conservationists alike. If we wish to remain comfortably within our existing forest and nature conservation paradigms, then addressing climate change has to remain our highest priority ... Sustaining the status quo for forestry or nature conservation alike will sadly no longer be an option.

As Spencer argues, one key response to reduce risks in the future is to diversify our forests in terms of their species composition and structure – in other words, a more balanced use of the four options outlined earlier. We also need to ensure that any future changes in silviculture have a sound scientific basis. In its first century the Forestry Commission has been pivotal in doubling the forest area in Britain, an achievement that would have been inconceivable without the growth and development of the theory and practice of silviculture. The challenges British forests face in the 21st century can seem daunting, but they herald a vigorous revival of the tradition of bold and learned silvicultural practice which will play a key role in ensuring that our nations' forests continue to thrive.

# CHAPTER 2

# Habitats

*The Wildlife and Environment of the*
*Forestry Commission Estate in England*

With the re-establishment of the nation's timber reserve as its primary objective after the depredations of both world wars the Forestry Commission pushed planting targets to their limits, afforesting bogs and mires, moors and heaths, planting even the most unpromising areas of limestone pavement and rocky outcrops. The Commission's approach to forestry practice and afforestation between the 1950s and '70s had a considerable impact on the nature and character of the nation's historic landscape. The Commission was party to the damage and loss of upland moors and mires, lowland heath and the many ancient woodlands within its care – all of which was loudly decried by naturalists and many others concerned about the future of the English landscape.

All that changed in the 1970s and 1980s. The Forestry Commission, and notably Forest Enterprise England (now Forestry England – that part of the Commission charged with managing the forest estate in England on behalf of the government), has gone through a Damascene conversion. In full recognition of the importance of people and of their deep concern for wildlife, ancient habitats and historical heritage, the Commission has recruited in-house ecological expertise, undertaken or supported extensive surveys and wildlife conservation programmes, released the imagination and commitment of staff, taken full advantage of their own and outside funding, and pursued the Herculean tasks of restoration, recovery, reinstatement and reintroduction.

# The Locust Years

In a memorable biblical phrase, the naturalist academic and author Oliver Rackham of Corpus Christi, Cambridge, described the period between 1950 and 1975 as 'the years that the locust hath eaten'. He was alluding to the massive utilitarian post-war drive to modernise the production of food and fibre and later to capitalise on the green revolution initiated in the 1960s. Big machines, high yielding crops, pesticides, insecticides, modern drainage and cropping patterns, supported by grant and subsidy, led to the loss of meadows and hedgerows, grazing marsh and inbye land, fields, walls, gates and paths that had been created over centuries and reflected both the character of the land and the individuality of those who had worked it with manual labour.

It was not only land that was affected: rivers were straightened, streams turned into canals, saltmarshes 'reclaimed' – the phrase itself implying that farmland was the natural order of things – small woods and copses removed, and heaths ploughed or planted with trees. The changes were profound and probably unparalleled since the enclosures of the 18th and 19th centuries. The very landscape was perceived as being under threat of extinction, along with the wildlife that it supported and the traditional practices that had created it.

At the end of the Second World War the Forestry Commission was still a fairly new creation, little more than 25 years old, and saw itself as at the forefront of modern forest practice: new production techniques, new management approaches, and cost-benefit analyses pressed hard. Pushed to the marginal lands of heathland and moorland by the demands of agricultural policies similarly driven by production, profit and performance, forestry was obliged to deliver its mandated vision of creating a viable national forest – and in turn a viable forest industry – onto the very marginal land where both history and natural history remained at their richest. The marginal land it could acquire was in the upland moors, on lowland heaths and within existing old woods – all places where cherished wildlife was to be found and landscapes were loved. The moors of Northumberland and Cumberland gave rise to Kielder Forest, the sandy heathy brecks of Norfolk to the origins of Thetford Forest, and plantations of spruce and Douglas fir were established in and among the ancient oaks of Sherwood and the New Forest. The plants, birds and animals of moors and heaths, old coppices and native woodlands disappeared as dense plantations of spruce were established across the hills and of conifers or beech in place of hazel and ash, oak and maple. At its zenith the zeal for modernisation led to the folly of young maturing oaks being poisoned and replaced with crops of spruce in the belief that over time it would be more economic to start again with the fast-growing conifers than let the rotation of oak complete its course. This of course proved to be a forest management disaster – and a public relations disaster. The Forestry Commission was seen as partly responsible for Rackham's 'Locust Years'.

Following a decade of challenge and crisis over ancient woodlands, afforestation of Sites of Special Scientific Interest (SSSIs), and most notoriously Commission support for privately funded planting schemes on the wet peatland wilderness of the area known as the Flow Country in Sutherland and Caithness in north-east Scotland (see Section 1, p. 78), there was a change of direction in the 1980s and '90s. The case for restoration of ancient woodlands in lowland landscapes was effectively made, most notably by Rackham who hosted courses attended by a great many Forestry Commission staff and whose erudition and charm brought many around to his way of thinking. (Heathlands came onto the script rather later, as their rarity in European terms and the spectacular suite of specialist wildlife became more widely appreciated.) Many staff, while committed to their vocations as foresters, were also keenly interested in wildlife, history or landscape – some passionately so. The change was also driven by both political reality (people wanted these things from their forests) and a maturing understanding of forest economics. The forests were entering into the felling and harvesting phases decades after their establishment as plantations and it was becoming clear that the original thinking and the earlier naïve assumptions about replanting costs, based on open conditions and pest- and deer-free landscapes, would have to be reconsidered. Uneconomic levels of investment in planting and establishment against the grain of nature simply did not stack up against the common sense of working with natural regeneration in ancient woods or withdrawing from forestry entirely in wet peats and mires.

# The Drivers of Change

The conservation of forest wildlife had increasingly featured in the thinking of the foresters driving forward the establishment of forests as the 20th century went on. The Commission was at the forefront of the conservation of birds of prey, and was very active in the conservation of red and roe deer. It pioneered the reintroduction of wild animals to its forests, most notably in Grizedale Forest in Cumbria where lakes and tarns were created for wildfowl, and an active role was played in the reintroduction of the greylag goose, then extinct in England as a breeding bird, in partnership with the then Wildfowlers' Association of Great Britain. The European beaver was first mooted for reintroduction to the UK by Forestry Commission Rangers and Foresters in Grizedale in the 1960s, only to be halted by the then Nature Conservancy (predecessor of English Nature and Natural England), concerned about the potential impact on native plants.

The winds began to change very much for the better for both the Forestry Commission and the planet with what became known as the Earth Summit in Rio de Janeiro in 1992. Rio set the agenda for establishing a sustainable world and virtually all nations signed up to its commitments. From Rio sprang both the Convention on Biological Diversity and – of key importance for the Forestry Commission – the Ministerial Conference on the Protection of Forests in Europe, known as the Helsinki Conference, held in 1993 and at which the basis for economically and ecologically sustainable forestry was established. Members of the Commission were at Helsinki, and the Commission soon afterwards set out its aims and objectives and how it would strive to meet them in accordance with a published Environmental Code:

> We believe the national forests should be places for people to enjoy, places where wildlife is encouraged, where rare natural and historical features are protected, and places where timber is produced for the market in an ecologically sustainable way.

This vision chimed neatly with the objectives of sustainable forestry set out in a number of other international forestry agreements, most notably the Statement on Forest Principles and the Biodiversity Convention which had been adopted at the 1992 Earth Summit. The Forestry Commission announced at the Helsinki Conference that it was launching a biodiversity initiative. The UK's plans for the implementation of the Forest Principles were then revealed by Prime Minister John Major in January 1994, in a publication entitled *Sustainable Forestry: The UK Programme*, pulling together the various strands of the government's forestry policies and actions both at home and overseas.

These international efforts were matched by policy developments at home. Interest in forest ecology had grown through the 1970s and 1980s: researchers and nature conservation organisations were becoming acutely aware of the threat to some species and ecosystems resulting from modern forestry methods. This increased awareness led to a commitment not only to safeguard conservation resources and natural ecosystems, but also to manage them accordingly. In the Commission's forest estate the expansion of native woodlands, the management of SSSIs, heathland conservation and management, and a wide range of wildlife conservation projects aimed at particular species were initiated nationally. The Commission's stewardship of the many sites of key importance for the nation's heritage was also becoming recognised: scattered throughout its estate are prehistoric forts, barrows and field systems, medieval settlements, military roads and bridges, rabbit traps, warreners' lodges, wartime installations, trenches, dugouts and pits, as well as many buildings of agricultural and industrial interest. Projects to improve access to these sites, and to increase the public's appreciation of them, also began. In the Forest of Dean, volunteers have created an app as part of the Foresters' Forest programme that unearths hidden heritage along trails within the Forest. The area has a rich industrial past and was once home to iron and coal mines, quarries and railways, but some of this heritage was in danger of being lost. Passionate community members trawled through photographic archives to uncover historic images of the forest, allowing members of the public to see how the landscape of the forest has changed.

The international agreements at Rio and Helsinki legitimised the environmental stewardship and conservation role of the Forestry Commission across the massive forest estate it had either inherited or created. The slow but steady emergence of multipurpose forestry

Golden larch *(Pseudolarix amabilis)*

in the 20th century was a direct outcome of this and is now backed by an independent certification scheme guaranteeing environmental and forestry excellence. The Commission supports the employment of a skilled and varied workforce delivering tangible products alongside the conservation of biodiversity, wildlife, historic fabric, environmental quality and, increasingly, environmental resilience.

# Restoration and Recovery of Ancient Habitats

There are some 50,000 hectares of ancient woodland on the public forest estate across England, and all are under restoration plans that reflect both their ancient pasts and their future role as providers of timber and wood fuel. The New Forest is on track for the full restoration of its ancient fabric of pasture, woods, heaths, mires and lawns, along with the restoration of mires, bogs and 'inclosures' (the areas within the forest established by statute for the purpose of timber production and whose individual character varies greatly according to past and recent history). The rivers and streams in the New Forest, much damaged by 19th- and 20th-century drainage, are being restored, re-establishing old river courses – adding tens of kilometres of river and stream to the south of England in the process – and the much-eroded river beds are being repaired. Similar river restoration projects are being planned in other forests, though on a rather more restrained scale, from Northumberland to Norfolk. Huge areas of upland mire in Northumberland are under steady restoration programmes as the sphagnum and bog mosses recover following major works to undrain drains, remove planted trees, and restore the past hydrology. Meadows and grassland are also being created or restored across England – especially grassland rides and the open, thin, sandy soils and sparse grassland of the Norfolk and Suffolk Breckland that support so many rare insects and annual plants.

Heathland is being widely restored, especially in the species-rich heartlands of the New Forest, Dorset and the Brecks, and in Devon,

Staffordshire, Nottinghamshire and Yorkshire. Veteran trees, locked in by vigorous growth of young native trees or planted conifers, are being freed from surrounding competition to prolong their already long lives and provide the habitat for the rare insects, fungi, lichens and mosses that can only be found on such veterans. Ryedale in Yorkshire is home to some of the oldest lime trees in the country; here as elsewhere veteran trees represent habitats that cannot quickly be recreated – they have evolved over hundreds of years – and the core conservation strategy has to be the retention of those we have for as long as possible.

# Ancient Woodlands

The idea of ancient woodland is far from new, but in the 1980s ancient woods – woodland that had persisted in the landscape for centuries as a source of timber and fuel for generations of our forebears – came into play as a major bone of contention between conservation organisations and the Forestry Commission. Ancient woodland was championed by two key players: Oliver Rackham and George Peterken, the senior woodland ecologist with the Nature Conservancy Council, who took the rapidly growing understanding of the origins and natural history of our ancient woods and forests and skilfully applied it to the development of conservation policy and management options. The compelling historical and ecological case, combined with the deep interest stirred within Commission foresters and woodland owners in the historic origins of their woods (and of their profession), led to swift acceptance of the importance and different silvicultural future that ancient woodlands represented. In 1985 the Commission launched its first Broadleaved Woodland Policy, identifying ancient woodland as deserving of special treatment.

During the 1990s, as Forestry Commission staff attended Rackham's courses on ancient woodland and their past history of management, the Nature Conservancy Council mapped and counted all the possible ancient woodland across England, Scotland and Wales in what became the Ancient Woodland Inventory. A little later, in 2002, the Commission undertook and published a survey of the extent and condition of all the ancient woodland then owned or managed by Forest Enterprise England. It then undertook to conserve its resource of ancient semi-natural woodland, and to restore to native woodland all the 35,000 hectares of plantations on ancient woodland sites that were in its care. The details of the 2002 survey revealed some powerful insights into our ancient woodland legacy. In England, the Forestry Commission owned or managed 23 per cent of the total woodland and forest area (219,143 hectares), 15 per cent of the total area of ancient woodland (53,128 hectares) and over 7 per cent of ancient semi-natural woodland (15,952 hectares). It had responsibility for the restoration of 26 per cent of the Plantations of Ancient Woodland sites (PAWS) (35, 426 hectares).

In 2005 Forestry Commission England published its first major policy on ancient woodland, *Keepers of Time: A Statement of Policy for England's Ancient and Native Woodland*, which laid out the policy and grant support framework for the conservation and State aid support available for ancient woodland across the country. And in 2006 the very last Corsican pine planted in the exemplary Chalkney Wood in Essex was felled by Rackham, marking the first wood in the country to be restored to a fully functioning ancient semi-natural woodland.

Past management policy and treatment have determined the character of these woods at the turn of the 21st century. Damaged by wartime need and subsequent attempts at establishing plantations on old woodland sites, most of the area of ancient woodland under the Commission's management developed as plantations of conifers, or beech and very occasionally oak, on what was clearly old native woodland managed as coppice or coppice with standards (where timber trees are grown on longer rotations among coppice cut on short rotations for poles or fuelwood).

There were some very notable exceptions. Shrawley Wood in Worcestershire, Bedford Purlieus in Northamptonshire, and the ancient and ornamental woods of the New Forest are all first-class examples of well-documented and wildlife-rich ancient woodlands that survived the utilitarian post-war decades to become some of the premier woodland sites in the country. To them can be added many other key sites, damaged and often then neglected but retaining features and potential of national importance; for example, the Lincolnshire limewoods, the Wyre Forest and of course, Chalkney Wood. The dire plight of the woods described by Rackham during those 'Locust Years' was not always reflected in the sites themselves as they could be found in 2002. The worst fears about the fate of large areas of ancient woodland had proven to be misplaced. The astonishing powers of recovery and regrowth of native trees and the resilience of ancient woods were clearly demonstrated in the 2002 survey, and subsequent restoration and recovery through planned forestry interventions aimed at their restoration are proving to be extremely effective. Time and considered action are leading to an ever-growing area of native woodland on ancient woodlands across the country. Oliver Rackham, in several letters to Forestry Commission staff in the years before his death in 2015, repeatedly expressed his delight at the Commission's successes in this area.

In practice much of the planned conversion to conifer was compromised by increasingly high costs in what were essentially labour-intensive activities (cleaning and early thinning) with little or no early return. Underplanted areas, mixed stands and extensive natural regeneration or regrowth of native trees conspired to flout the intentions of the foresters of the Commission. Some planted tree species did not perform as well as anticipated, particularly on heavier clay soils. The widespread variety and nature of the woodlands, with sites on virtually all geological formations across the country, and the vicissitudes of subsequent management history (with some stands receiving little or none of the planned silvicultural input, and others managed to the highest standards) led to an astonishing variety of responses that shaped the subsequent stands to be found on Plantations on Ancient Woodland Sites (PAWS) across the country. Experience had shown that the recovery of native woodland following the removal of the planted stands could either be quite spectacular, even in stands with little or no obvious capacity for recovery, or spectacularly disappointing. Plantations of conifer on base rich clay soils fared worst, those on rich acid sandy loams the best, often producing first-class stands of conifer timber. Both showed potential for considerable recovery and all had remnant features particularly on their boundaries. Stands on sandy acid soils presented the hardest choices: they were readily restorable to oak and birch but highly productive as non-native conifers, or in some instances impossible to return to anything akin to their original native woodland character, with vigorous established growth and widespread regeneration of western hemlock and Douglas fir. In virtually all cases the damage to trees inflicted by the introduced grey squirrels has thoroughly compromised any potential future timber quality from native and other broadleaved trees.

The 2002 survey established the extent and nature of the challenge, the financial costs, and the environmental benefits of changing the character of the suite of ancient woodland under the Commission's charge, and the impact of any policy options on forest income and timber production forecasts. In the event the decision was made to restore as much as possible of the ancient woodland to native, managed forest, over a timescale that reflected the economic maturity of stands and the immediate benefits of clearing up those that had, in effect, restored themselves in the later years of the 20th century.

This programme continues to the present day. As they have come up for renewal, Forest Plans have accommodated and furthered the restoration of ancient woodland and brought existing ancient semi-natural woods into active management and production. Programmes of thinning and removal of non-native planted trees and enrichment planting, particularly of oak, have progressively brought more and more PAWS into what could be classed as restored native woodland. After massive initial steps forward as the woods where native tree species had already asserted themselves among the planted stands were tackled, progress has slowed and work has settled into the steady round of thinning and restocking as stands develop and slowly reach an economic age to fell. Several key challenges have emerged that still require thought and continued commitment. Deer have become an ever-greater problem and often thwart attempts to recruit new stands of naturally regenerated or planted native trees, and to recover the flora characteristic of old woodland. The Commission has frequently had to resort to fencing alongside more active deer management and control. Grey squirrels compromise the quality of broadleaved trees being grown for timber, damaging the younger branches and allowing rot and disease into the wounds inflicted on the bark. They have also thwarted the spread of hazel, consuming the nuts well before they are ripe! Many species of planted conifers, but notably Douglas fir and western hemlock, hold to their own agendas and throw down copious amounts of viable seed that readily recruits into future mixed stands. Rhododendron has to be thoroughly eradicated as it smothers vegetation and changes the character of the soils to exclude all species but its own. The growing threats from climate change and the arrival of novel pests and pathogens challenge our very notion of restoration to some past condition of utilisable native trees and shrubs. Ash dieback looks to compromise the future abundance of ash (the most useful and versatile of our native timber trees, readily recruiting from seed, readily growing as coppice regrowth, and of great value as firewood, small wood and timber). Oaks are suffering from squirrel damage and threatened by a variety of diseases and cankers; beeches suffer from drought and are very prone to squirrel attack; sweet chestnut now has both blights and gall wasps to contend with; and non-native trees of varying degrees of acceptability – western hemlock and Douglas fir, sycamore and Norway maple – are all poised to move into the spaces created by the demise of much-loved and favoured traditionally used trees. Ancient woodland restoration is proving in practice to be far more complex and challenging than appeared at the turn of the century.

# Future Forests

As the extensive plantations of spruce, pine and other conifers mature into new forests with up to a century of development and change behind them, they are surprising many as their ecology evolves and unfolds, with species of birds, plants and animals finding them much to their liking and colonising the new spaces and places that support them as they grow, reproduce or overwinter. This has been most remarkable with the birds of the extensive new forests. Although some birds appear to have been lost forever – the wheatears of the Brecks or north Norfolk and the black grouse of the high Pennine moors – many more species have thrived and surprised: goshawks in the spruce forests of north and western Britain; nightjars and woodlarks in the pine forests of the south and east; ospreys in forests near to coast or inland water; crossbills and siskins in the pines; turtle doves in woods and thicket stage forests in East Anglia; long-eared owls in dense stands in lonely woods and dark corners. And on lowland heaths most of the birds, insects, reptiles and plants of heathland that once lived on open heath now thrive in the clearfells and sandy, heathy rides associated with pine forests that mimic the sandy boreal pine forests of northern Europe. Only on Forestry Commission forests can one find all six of our native reptiles (adder, sand lizard, slow-worm, grass snake, common lizard and smooth snake) living alongside goshawks, nightjars and crossbills.

By the turn of the century it was becoming clear that although losses had undoubtedly occurred, considerable gains in wildlife had also been accrued. Newly established forests were developing an ecology peculiar to themselves, reflecting their particular management, derived in large part from the original planted land, supplemented by many new arrivals and the occasional deliberate reintroduction, such as pool frogs in Thetford Forest or white-faced darter dragonflies in Cheshire. With the damage being reversed in so many locations across the country and a 'future natural' ecology emerging strongly in our non-native production forests of spruce, pine and larch, the Forestry Commission in England has become, after a century of challenge, effort and change, a major player in the conservation of the biodiversity of the UK across its large and varied estate.

As the Commission marks its centenary, the environmental position of the forests looks promising. Following the employment of their first full-time professional ecologist in the New Forest in 1995, Forest Districts now employ no fewer than ten professional ecologists and around fifty Wildlife Rangers, assisted by a diverse national team including a Head of Forest Environment and Planning, Lead Wildlife Ranger Manager and Head of Heritage, all devoted in full or in large part to the conservation and management of our forests and the wildlife they support.

# Seeds of Recovery

The year 2010 marked a major milestone in the history of wildlife and nature conservation in the Forestry Commission. In that year Forest Enterprise England (now Forestry England) concluded its major programme of SSSI recovery, and reached the dizzy heights of getting over 99 per cent of the SSSIs owned or managed by the Commission in England into 'favourable' or 'favourable recovering' target condition, against a national target of 95 per cent. The target conditions were independently set and assessed by English Nature (now Natural England), the government's nature conservation agency. It was a major achievement exceeded by no other government agency. The programme was part of the much wider biodiversity targets set by the government in 2003 and led by its key government institutions, English Nature, the Environment Agency, the Ministry of Defence (with a major stake in the programme given the extent of such designated land on its military training grounds such as Salisbury Plain and elsewhere), and of course the Forestry Commission.

The Commission in England had an unusual role: not only did it directly own or manage some 68,000 hectares of land designated as SSSI, Special Protection Areas (SPA), relating particularly to wild birds, and Special Areas of Conservation (SAC), relating particularly to habitat and species conservation of international significance, with some additional National Nature Reserves alongside, but it also had a policy and support role in delivering SSSI condition beyond its own estate in woodlands where SSSI condition was dependent on actions supported by the Commission. In some sites, woodlands required management or protection from deer; in others – overgrown fens, heathlands carrying plantations – trees and plantations, and the need for their removal, were part of the problem rather than the solution, in extensive scrub or tree growth on chalk downs for example. The Forestry Commission played a key role in effecting change. In the seven years of the programme (2003–10), the Commission, through the expertise and skills of its staff, efforts and actions on its own lands, and through grant support, advice and policy changes elsewhere, shifted thousands of hectares of designated land from SSSI originally identified as in unfavourable or declining condition by English Nature into target condition. In time, action on these sites would lead to a full recovery of the habitat and associated species identified as a key reason for designation as a site of national importance.

The fact that over 99 per cent of the landholding designated as SSSI reached the target condition of either favourable condition or recovering status by 2010, was the result of seven years of careful planning and costing, restoration work, conservation management and effort by the operational staff. Many of the sites themselves were those damaged by earlier drainage or afforestation operations during the 'Locust Years', leading at least one notable conservationist to quip that the Forestry Commission's favourite category of SSSI was the one it had messed up earlier! The condition of SSSI has been maintained ever since with a growing percentage deemed in 'favourable' condition each year as time and continued effort shifts them from recovery to sustained good condition.

The reputation of the Forestry Commission has benefited as a result and it is now seen as a key partner in environmental management and wildlife conservation projects across England, and an important participant in the conservation of our wildlife legacy and the creation of new wildlife rich landscapes for the future. The programme also brought to the fore the solid practical capabilities, commitment and sheer competence of the staff engaged in the programme, as hundreds of thousands of tonnes of timber, gravel or ditch-filling materials, millions of pounds of resources in the form of materials and labour, and tens of thousands of hectares of land were expertly deployed to great effect to deliver the target aim of getting its SSSIs into a condition to face the coming century.

# 'Future Natural'

The last few decades have seen a great increase in the Forestry Commission's understanding of how forests work in their underlying ecology, the role of keystone species, and the drivers of diversity and change. At the same time it has an increasing appreciation of the social and environmental benefits of forests and the key role that timber and fibre production will play in the creation of a low carbon landscape and economy. And hovering over all is an emerging understanding of how much challenge and change are coming in the form of climate change and the globalisation of trade, bringing with them exposure to novel insect pests and tree diseases, and how best to thrive under the new conditions as they emerge.

Scots pine *(Pinus sylvestris)*

In its approach to nature conservation in the forests under its stewardship in the 21st century, the Forestry Commission is now looking far more closely at forest resilience, based on a sound understanding of forest ecology, biodiversity, and the care of forest soils. It is carefully exploring the rebuilding of forest ecosystems from its components, while maintaining the flow of products necessary to build a low carbon future. New projects and programmes are aimed at sustainable wildlife habitat management and the restoration of key species that drive forest ecology and diversity: the use of heathland arisings to generate renewable energy to mimic the extractive use of heaths in the past; the recovery of birds of prey, butterflies and other wildlife lost from our forests; and the measured reintroduction of wild animals upon which key processes in forest ecology depend – otters and ospreys moving key plant nutrients into the forests from lake and stream; beavers to create riparian habitat rich in wildlife, cleaning and holding back water with their dams and pools; pine martens to drive down the number of grey squirrels and pave the way ahead for the recovery and return of the red; cattle to mimic the role of aurochs in the past. To this list can be added many lesser players that add to both our enjoyment of the forest and its functioning, rather than simply woodland wildlife: water voles as primary herbivores, hoverflies and butterflies and other pollinators, deadwood and the fungal diversity it supports, and mature and veteran trees that host some of the rarest and most restricted of woodland plants, insects and fungi.

Embracing a broader understanding of ecological process and interaction is leading the Commission and others away from individual and often heavily subsidised, historical land-use-based conservation management. This is a complex and challenging programme: maintaining the forest management for timber harvesting and the restocking of felled areas, while simultaneously conserving the legacy sites of ancient semi-natural habitat that were inherited at the time of acquisition; restoring and creating habitat as part of the evolving forest's character; putting scarce resources into sustaining relict populations of rare and unusual plants and animals that have persisted from the past, so as not to lose them entirely, while investing in projects aimed at establishing stronger and more robust populations responding to the conditions created by forest management and activity -- all going on alongside the work of supporting the existing demands for timber, woodfuel, fibre or recreation. The Commission is exploring the role of 'wilderness' and 'rewilding', while finding 21st-century markets for traditional hay cutting of meadows and rides, and modern outlets for traditional coppice approaches to woodland management. It's a heady mix of objectives and outcomes, with different woods and forests presenting different opportunities and challenges.

Across the woods and forests that make up the public forest estate there are species that have persisted or returned, new species that have arrived and thrived – or have arrived and remained rare – and new habitats that have been created and, over the best part of a century, become vested with a wide range of native wildlife in novel ecosystems. The hoverflies and beetles, fungi and plants that have naturally colonised the Commission's evolving forests have become part of the 'future natural' condition of plantations and woods established over the 20th century. Although this cannot be said with certainty, it is thought that some 70–80 per cent of all the terrestrial species listed as of particular note in England occur somewhere within the woods and forests, moors and heaths managed by the Forestry Commission. One remaining task for the coming century will be to find out what the Commission has, where it is located, and what it means. This will constitute as big a legacy of the past hundred years of forest development as the forests within which these species can be found.

# CHAPTER 3

# Forest Science

F orest science is an essential element in the success of forestry, and the contribution of the Commission and its scientists and researchers has dominated the field right across the UK. Some of these these scientists have become recognised globally as leaders in their own disciplines, some have built and maintained respect and reputation nationally for their expertise and advisory work, others have been unsung heroes, but without their work over the last hundred years much of what has been achieved in British forestry would have been impossible. Research and data services in the UK are centred around the Alice Holt Research Station near Farnham in Surrey and the Northern Research Station near Edinburgh. However, since environment and geography have very major effects on how science works and is applied, research and trial work also continues to be done across Scotland, England and Wales. Research and associated extension work is now managed to optimise the integration of people into multidisciplinary teams and to encourage interaction and partnership working with other UK and international organisations.

## Forest Science and Data Services

The range of skills important to the provision of the forest science and data services which British forestry needs to flourish is considerable. It includes not only areas of forest science self-evidently critical to productive forestry such as silviculture, forest management, modelling and production forecasting, timber quality, wood science and tree breeding, but also important disciplines in environmental science including forest ecology, forest hydrology, entomology and forest pathology, urban forestry and land regeneration, soil science, climate change science, genetics and molecular biology, and other relevant and underpinning specialisms, notably statistics, economics, social science, Geographical Information Systems, decision support and programming, communications and knowledge exchange.

Access to these areas of expertise is valuable to British forestry, and building and maintaining a comprehensive set of forest science skills have been among the Commission's major achievements. However, forest science has progressed incrementally rather than by sudden revelation and the major developments are perhaps more evident with hindsight. These have included research on species choice and tree breeding for the expansion of forest cover in the uplands, the associated work to develop the necessary silviculture (ground preparation, phosphate application etc.) for the impressive increase of Britain's forest cover, the science to support forest planning and wood utilisation (yield tables, production forecast and timber quality work), the realisation of how important broadleaved woodlands are to people and landscape, work on biodiversity and conservation of woodland species, and critically important work on forest and tree protection (pathology and entomology).

# The Early Years

By the time that the Forestry Commission was established in 1919, introduced species were present and valued in Britain and a well-established tradition of woodland management, plantations, coppicing, pollarding and the nurturing of standards already existed. A number of the great arboreta had also been established. Largely as a result of work done on a few private estates and the much stronger tradition of State forestry in mainland Europe, there was also some limited understanding of how woodland creation could be achieved using native and introduced broadleaves and conifers.

The challenge that confronted the Forestry Commission on its establishment was substantial and it was understood that good-quality forest science, although it had had little impact on UK forestry up to that time, would be essential to meet it. The first Annual Report of the Forestry Commission (1920) describes British forestry research as being in its infancy:

> Admirable as had been the pioneering work done by individuals and by the forestry societies, it had seldom been directed to those particular points which were of importance to a forest authority initiating state forestry *ab ovo*.

Recognising that this needed to change, the third of the Commissioners' six initial objectives was

> The endowment of research at a limited number of centres and – without interfering with that liberty of action so necessary to scientific progress – the general direction of research to the problems of immediate importance.

Responsibility for delivery of the Commissioners' objectives across the country had been passed to 11 Divisional Officers and 25 District Officers, but staff were appointed at the Commission's headquarters for control of policy, finance, education, research and publications. Accordingly in its first year the Forestry Commission appointed an Education and Publications Officer, a Research Officer, an Entomologist and a Co-ordination Officer ('to secure co-ordination in technical procedure throughout the different parts of the United Kingdom').

The first cohort of Commissioners was clearly concerned to have research support that directly addressed the practical requirements. The first five publications of the Forestry Commission addressed the 'Rate of Growth of Timber' (*Bulletin* 1), a 'Survey of the Forest Insect Conditions in the British Isles' (*Bulletin* 2), the 'Rate of Growth of Conifers in the British Isles' (*Bulletin* 3), 'The Large Pine Weevil (*Hylobius abietis*)' (*Leaflet* 1), and a statement and programme for the British Empire Forestry conference of 1920. Two of the Commission's great publication series (the Bulletins and Leaflets) had been initiated. The Commission had also funded work on fungal diseases at the University of Oxford which resulted in the publication of an account of the fungal diseases of larch. A close link had been established between policy and operational objectives and the research that the Commission would fund or carry out itself. This close link and the strongly applied approach to forest research remain important to the Commission's research agency, Forest Research, and to UK forestry today. The story of the research staff and the science they provided is closely interwoven with the changes in policy and the achievements of British forestry. Some people in Research moved back to operational roles in the Commission and the private sector, giving their experience and enthusiasm direct application. Other research staff were given the freedom to remain in research and to become acknowledged authorities.

R. F. Wood, the Commission's Chief Research Officer, provided a professionally written and comprehensive account of the first 50 years of Forestry Commission research in *Bulletin* 50. This fascinating and detailed piece covers the organisational context – including the history of the Commission between 1920 and 1970 – and how research addressed the issues. Much of what was initiated over the first 50 years survives as published information, and also physically as sample plots and forest experiments (see the Appendix, p. 156). British achievements in forest science prior to the establishment of the Commission were the establishment in the late 19th century of the forest gardens in England, Ireland and Wales (i.e. the start of the systematic work on species which continues today, focused largely around achieving diversity and adaptation to climate change), and the work done at Kew on the hybridisation of forest trees to increase vigour. Our main upland forestry species predate 1919; however, the Commission's research continued this approach and can take credit for the establishment of Sitka spruce, Douglas fir, Corsican pine, hybrid larch, Norway spruce and lodgepole pine as main forestry species. According to Wood's account of research prior to the establishment of the Commission, it is difficult to separate forest research from the 'general legacy of the past; from the plant and soil sciences, arboriculture and pioneering forestry, and from the European professional tradition'. One of the main impacts of the Commission would be the initiation, organisation and coordination of a much more substantial body of forestry research in Britain.

Research by the Commission developed a sound set of systems to record the high-quality experimental work being established in its forests. Every forest experiment had a unique reference number: the first part was the name of the forest in which it was located and the second was a sequenced number based on how many previous experiments had been established in the same forest. Experimental files were maintained to a high standard and completed by successive staff as they served periods in research. These forest trials were often large-scale, long-lived and 'cutting edge' in what they achieved. Some of those which continue to have an impact on forest science appear in the Appendix, p. 156.

# The Forestry Commission's Research Division

After 1945 the Forestry Commission created its own research institute by establishing Forest Research at Alice Holt Lodge. This was a major milestone in the organisation of research, as was the later setting-up of the Northern Research Station at Roslin in 1973. Forestry Commission objectives and the associated forestry research priorities diversified over the period from 1945 to 1970 and thereafter, although the emphasis on selection, production and establishment of the new woodlands required by Britain remains evident as does the sense of urgency and the strong practical approach.

The move of Forest Research to Alice Holt and the subsequent establishment of the Northern Research Station consolidated the decision to provide much of the Forestry Commission's research from within the organisation rather than the alternative approach of commissioning only from the universities. The view of Roy Robinson, a former Commissioner and from 1932 Chairman of the Board of Commissioners, was that Commission research had to be practice-oriented and of direct value to the afforestation programme which he had been so instrumental in drawing up. He felt that the scientist needed to be in the forest working with operational staff to achieve the best practice and management. As Chairman he was closely involved in research and greatly respected: he is considered the 'father of Forestry Commission research'.

Fred Hummel, who later developed the Forestry Commission's standard methods for measuring standing crops (the tariff system) and went on to do forestry work for the UN Food and Agriculture Organization, the UN Development Programme and the European Community, gave the following account of his arrival at Alice Holt in September 1946:

> When I came in '46 in September, there was only one other occupant here. That was Tom Peace, our pathologist. Many of you will still remember him, because afterwards he became the Chief Research Officer ... Now, I arrived and the first thing that Tom said was, 'Fred, I'm terribly sorry, I can show you round but there's only one chair and one table in this building, so would you mind working from home until we can get a second chair?' He was willing to share the table! We looked around the place and it was rather sad and neglected.

If a business is producing wood or indeed the development of an effective national forestry policy, it is sensible to record the growth of different tree species at a number of sites across the country for at least one rotation, preferably more. A refinement would be to manage these sample plots differently – e.g. grow the species pure and in mixtures or test different thinning regimes and record the effects. This is essentially what the Forestry Commission's permanent sample plot network is and in some instances the plots have been maintained and measured since the Commission took them over on its establishment. The late 1940s saw an expansion of the permanent sample plot network and development of the Yield Class system which drew on the data they provided. This elegant system, one of the foundations of forest management, was a world first (see Chapter 1 p. 100). Now available online, it remains fundamentally as designed at that time and is still critical to forestry in Britain. It was developed over a period when forest economics was the cornerstone of much of the research and policy thinking in British forestry. Indeed, *Forest Planning* (1967) by David Johnston, Arnold Grayson and Roger Bradley remains a classic. While they worked at Alice Holt these three were an intellectual powerhouse. They went on to senior roles and were feared and respected in equal measure.

By 1957 important work had unequivocally shown that the application of phosphate was essential to the establishment of conifers on poor upland soils and John Zehetmayr had published two seminal bulletins on heath and peatland afforestation. Such work made the establishment of Britain's new upland forest estate possible.

Forest entomology and pathology had been recognised as important from the outset and Forest Research staff had monitored for presence, diagnosed causal agents, and where possible developed and recommended controls. The first indication of how serious introduced pathogens could be was the second Dutch elm disease outbreak in the late 1960s. Dutch elm disease had already been seen in Europe. The disease is caused by the fungus *Ophiostoma ulmi* which had been identified on a number of occasions in the UK, including a less aggressive epidemic between 1920 and 1940, but in 1967 a new and far more damaging – indeed lethal – strain of the pathogen arrived, resulting in an epidemic in which more than 25 million English elms were killed in the UK. English elm (*Ulmus procera*) is a magnificent tree which had dominated much of the British landscape largely as a hedgerow tree. It has subsequently become almost eliminated as a mature tree, although large amounts of hedgerow survive. Although not a major commercial species, by the time of Dutch elm disease, elm was highly valued for its beautiful wood, its distinctive form especially in hedgerows, and the unique habitat it provided for a large number of species. Detailed research over a number of years showed that the fungus causing the new virulent form of the disease (*Ophiostoma novo-ulmi*) had spread across the northern hemisphere in the second part of the 20th century, acquiring major genes through hybridisation with *Ophiostoma ulmi*. This was an early example of how unpredictable and devastating newly arrived pathogens can be and showed how important it is to understand the biology of disease agents in order to manage outbreaks and subsequent disease management.

# Organisation of Research

Before moving on to the much more diverse forestry policies of the 1980s onwards, it is worth saying something about how the work in the field was organised. Experiments on cultivation and drainage, establishment, weed control and stand management, and others were addressed by the powerhouse Silviculture Branches – Silv North and Silv South of the Research Division and later Forest Research. Two aspects of how research was organised were particularly led by the Silviculture Branches. One, the naming and filing systems for forest experiments, has already been mentioned. The other was the tour system, which was particularly effective for silviculture; this involved foresters moving in from other parts of the Forestry Commission for perhaps three years as project leaders in research before returning to Districts and Conservancies. The system broadened experience, developed skills and was good for career development, but was unpopular with other research organisations who found that no sooner had they got to know the person responsible for, say, the silviculture of broadleaved species, than that person was moved to run a Forest District.

The work of forest experimentation was largely undertaken by Outstation Foresters, which helped to address some of the issues created by the tour system. These research staff were located in offices spread across England, Scotland and Wales and were a critical part of the set-up for many years. Outstation Foresters and 'squads' were responsible for the establishment, monitoring and measurement of experiments, and reported to project leaders at the two research stations. Much depended on the personalities involved. Research suffered or perhaps benefited from what in the Districts was called 'the Boy DO' syndrome, although in Research it was the strictly the 'Boy Project Leader'. The issue was the same: a fresh-faced, newly qualified youngster would stand in front of a squad of experienced Outstation staff to tell them how he or she wanted things done – many of the outstation heads were highly committed, knowing their experiments well and how to do things. Often an experiment ran on quietly, being maintained and monitored without its project leader really knowing much about it! The Outstation staff also served as excellent contacts with forestry where they were located and were a highly effective extension service.

Gisburn 1, an experiment from 1955, is among the 'greats' of British forestry experiments and typifies the benefits of the systems described above. Generations of Research staff of all types must have looked after the experiment, travelling to a remote, wet and inhospitable but beautiful location high in the Pennines and not far from the Yorkshire Dales National Park. As a result of resilience and hard work, the experiment is now in its second rotation. Initially, its objective was to compare pure and mixed stands of Norway spruce (*Picea abies*), Scots pine (*Pinus sylvestris*), sessile oak (*Quercus petrea*) and common alder (*Alnus glutinosa*). At the end of the first rotation there was an enhanced growth in all mixtures with Scots pine but a negative interaction (poorer growth than pure stands) in the Norway spruce/sessile oak mixture. After wind-blow the experiment was felled and then replanted in 1991 with Sitka spruce (*Picea sitchensis*) added to the trial. Mixtures again proved beneficial with height and diameter growth considerably better in the Norway and Sitka spruce when in mixed plots. For three mixtures – Sitka spruce–Scots pine, Norway spruce–Scots pine, and Norway spruce–common alder – basal area growth was about 40 per cent greater than would have been predicted for pure stands of the same species. Forestry experiments that have gone beyond one rotation are rare throughout the world and in this experiment, which was written up by Bill Mason and Tom Connolly in an outstanding paper in 2014, the results support the case for diversification of single-species plantations in the British uplands.

# The Forestry Commission's Research Agency

In the late 1970s and early 1980s British forestry was growing steadily with the technical and scientific support it required, resulting in a genuine ethos of multipurpose forestry and a recognition of the need to allow access and provide public benefits including wildlife conservation.

Research focused on largely forestry subjects: silviculture, production forecasting, windthrow prediction, pathology and entomology to manage known problems. Species selection was considered to be largely solved and the programme of tree improvement in a conventional breeding programme was progressing well. At this point the likely impacts of climate change were yet to be fully appreciated.

The invention and development of tree shelters which were trialled from 1979 onwards revolutionised small-scale plantings. These translucent tubes are used to protect young trees from grazing, make weed-control easier and create a greenhouse-like environment which enhances growth and improves survival rates. In the first experiment in 1979 180 hand-made shelters were trialled; by 1984 well over one million had been sold in Britain and they had become an accepted forest practice. During the 1980s there was also a shift to undertake more research on broadleaves and much of this research contributed to the Broadleaves Policy Review published in July 1990.

The 1980s were a period of rapid political and social change with a growing public awareness of environmental issues including conservation, environmental pollution/acidification, the protection of water (quality and quantity) and soils, and in due course climate change, environmental sustainability and the protection of forests and trees against introduced organisms – mammals, fungal pathogens and insect pests. Most of these issues remain important today but from the 1980s onwards forestry came under scrutiny as a result of the part it plays in the environment and landscape (both nationally and worldwide). In responding to these increasingly publicised environmental concerns, the sector needed good authoritative research and scientific advice including in areas well beyond forest practice.

The linked issues of forest decline and water acidification are a good example of how science, policy and an opportunity for change (public and political support) came together and provided answers and a better outcome for the pubic and the environment. Forest declines occur in potentially all forest ecosystems and are often a natural phenomenon associated with ecological succession or changing climatic and site conditions. However, in the late 1970s and early 1980s the forest declines which were seen across central Europe and in Nordic countries appeared to be novel: they were widespread geographically and showed a degree

Bigleaf maple *(Acer macrophyllum)*

of synchrony, affecting a number of species, particularly Norway spruce, beech, silver fir and oak. At the same time salmon fisheries were declining in Scandinavia and Scotland, and lakes were becoming acidified. These environmental impacts led to strong public and media involvement and thus to political pressure. Government ministers, parliamentary select committees and the media were asking questions. Were tree species selection and forestry practice wrong and hence causing forest decline? Would we lose our woodlands? Were trees, particularly conifers, causing acidification of soils and freshwaters? These were questions that the forestry sector and the Forestry Commission's researchers had not considered before, even though there were UK scientists who understood forest soils and forest hydrology and had considerable expertise in forest entomology and pathology. A considerable amount of new research was needed and undertaken; in the UK this was mostly collaborative, involving Forest Research and scientists in the universities and research institutes. The results of this new work were published by review groups within the Department of the Environment, in science journals and in Forestry Commission publications. In due course the public and the government accepted the weight of scientific evidence that pollutant emissions (mainly of sulphur and nitrogen) were the major cause of the new wave of forest declines and that pollution, not forests, was driving environmental acidification. The mechanisms were complex but the overall conclusions were clear and, very importantly, the immediate problems – sulphur and nitrogen emissions – were tractable. The political and policy response followed logically and developments in the UK energy and transport sector presented opportunities for change (e.g. the switch from coal to gas for a major part of electricity generation and the fitting of catalytic converters to cars).

Although the sulphur and nitrogen abatement measures of the 1980s and early 1990s solved the immediate problems of forest decline and acidification of freshwater to a significant degree, they did not solve the much wider and more substantial issue of atmospheric pollution generally – far from it. Science was gathering an increasing understanding of climate change and here, as for environmental acidification, forests and woodlands were a critical element of the environmental and social changes involved. The argument could be made that climate change was a more threatening and widespread concern than acidification but in reality it is also a problem of pollutant emissions. UK forest science responded again to a major environmental issue with its associated public and political concerns. For Forest Research, major contributions to climate change research have been to understand carbon fluxes from the atmosphere to forests and then from forests on through the cycle of wood utilisation. The Commission and Forest Research together have also taken a lead in reviewing and presenting the relevant science, an important example being the publication in 2009 of the first national assessment of the role of forests in the mitigation of and adaptation to climate change.

The initiation of a long-term and well-resourced tree breeding programme can be dated back to 1948. As a result of this work, by the 1980s foresters throughout the UK were beginning to be able to plant improved tested material for most of the major conifer species. Tree breeding is a long-term business and the achievement owes much to the skills and enthusiasm of those involved. Sam Samuel, Allan John and Steve Lee summarised the achievements of the programme in their publication *Fifty Years of Tree Breeding in Great Britain* (2000). Between 1950 and 1992, 12,824 'plus' trees (the very best ones, identified as having superior characteristics) were selected for the breeding programme – the scale of the endeavour becomes clear! The greatest effort and thus improvement has been in the breeding of Sitka spruce (*Picea sitchensis*), for which gains in volume have been improved by about 23 per cent compared with controls. Today the tree breeding programme is as important as ever and the focus is on the production of species and genotypes which will be suitable for the climate of the future and resilient to major pests and pathogens.

The longer established concerns of the UK forestry sector – to have good planting stock of species which suit the site well; to have healthy, productive and well-managed woodlands which contribute to conservation and landscape – had not gone away. Indeed, some of these concerns, notable that of tree health, have risen in priority along with the changing environmental and social changes of the late 20th and early 21st centuries. Although the UK forest sector had been well aware of the threat from tree pathogens and damaging insects – pests – from the outset, it was the outbreaks of Dutch elm disease and the forest decline debate in the 1970s and 1980s that had first raised public concern over tree health. Subsequently public awareness of the ecological, landscape and economic impacts of tree pests and diseases diminished until a number of new outbreaks which occurred from 2003 onwards.

The rise in the number of new pests and pathogens arriving in the UK and causing problems has been attributed to the increased movement of goods, plant materials (live plants for planting or used in packaging) and people. This has introduced insects and pathogens to new potential hosts and exposed introduced exotic trees to endemic native pests and pathogens. In these circumstances, the lack of co-evolution involving both pathogen and host can mean that effective resistance mechanisms are largely absent so that pests and pathogens cause substantially greater damage. The outcome of novel associations are thus unpredictable but can be severely damaging to the host, and normal quarantine and phytosanitary control measures may be ineffective. Ash dieback (see Chapter 4 p. 180) is a good example of this new challenge, because while the established native species *Hymenoscyphus albidus* is responsible for undamaging fungal decay of ash leaves on the woodland floor, the newly arrived fungus *Hymenoscyphus fraxineus* has enhanced pathogenicity and is causing widespread tree death. This is now a major focus of forestry research in the UK. In the case of the other major current outbreak in UK forestry, the causal agent *Phytophthora ramorum* was introduced to the UK on other species, notably rhododendron, but then made a switch to European, Japanese and hybrid larch. Until the current outbreak of the disease, larch was very important to UK forestry both for timber production and, as the only deciduous conifer widespread in the UK, for its landscape and species diversity value. These events – the arrival of new pests and pathogens, the evolution of enhanced pathogenicity or a jump to a new host – can all challenge the effectiveness of plant health policy and the link between science and policy is thus critical in such areas – something that the UK has learnt in the last few years. As with other issues which had risen up the science and political agenda unexpectedly, the UK forestry sector was fortunate to have established and committed tree health experts ready to advise. Some of the most prominent scientists in this field are doing critical work in Forest Research and other institutions. Joan Webber, for example, was honoured with an OBE for her outstanding work on tree health.

# Forest Statistics and the National Forest Inventory

Over the past 100 years, the Forestry Commission has used statistics to describe its woodlands and to monitor how they change over time. Much of this statistical evidence was gathered through the Commission conducting six 'one-off' national woodland inventories every 10–20 years, the first in the 1920s and the last in the 1990s. These confirmed that in 1919 forest and woodland cover was estimated at around 1.2 million hectares – around 5 per cent of total land cover for Britain – and that throughout the century woodland area was expanding until by 2019 it stood at over 3 million hectares – around 13.4 per cent of land cover. That represents the establishment of around 2 million hectares of new woodland or a near tripling of woodland area in just 100 years.

The Commission's forest inventory scientists and statisticians have continuously improved their woodland survey techniques and by the late 2000s, in a world changing ever more rapidly, it was recognised that more detailed and frequent statistics on woodlands were required. In response to this, a permanent and ongoing National Forest Inventory (NFI) was designed by a team led by Ben Ditchburn, based upon a fusion of aerial photography, satellite technologies and advances in computing and fieldwork. This new approach enabled detailed monitoring of not only the area and timber potential of woodlands, but also their biodiversity and social value, health and overall ecological condition. The new NFI commenced in 2010 and over the next five years the Forestry Commission implemented the most in-depth survey of British woodlands in our history, in which forest surveyors visited over 15,000 sample sites across Britain, measuring and mapping over 700,000 individual trees and around 50,000 forest plots. The new approach soon found that we had 8 per cent more woodland area than previously thought and allowed for much greater accuracy in timber availability forecasts. In underpinning these forecasts the NFI supplies a window on the future of our forests and as a result since 2012 the Forestry Commission has supplied a series of long-term forecasts of forest growth, forest timber and carbon stocks, and timber availability.

The NFI also undertook a survey of trees outside woodland in 2017 and found that this accounted for 3.2 per cent of British land area. Taken in combination with the 13.4 per cent of woodland tree canopy cover, this gives an estimate of a total tree canopy cover in Britain of 16.5 per cent in urban areas and 16.7 per cent in rural areas – a green and pleasant land indeed. This survey also established that for every region in Britain, urban tree canopy cover amounts to around 16.5 per cent per city or town – a remarkable finding, almost as if people have an inbuilt preference for a certain amount of canopy cover to live within. This finding was reflected in the fact that 34 per cent of all lone trees are found in urban areas.

In the year of the Commission's centenary the NFI is publishing a wealth of new information on the extent, health and nature of our native woodland. The survey found that we had 1.45 million hectares of native woodland, rather than the one million previously thought. Also, in establishing the area of each of our native woodland habitats, it found that some woodland habitats such as wet woodland had around three times more area than previously thought. The data also includes the first ever national assessment of seedlings and saplings in our woods, showing us that they are present in around 80 per cent of native woodland stands. This is a positive indicator that we likely have enough young trees to maintain most of our native woodlands well into the future.

The Forestry Commission is currently undertaking the second cycle of the NFI (2015–20), revisiting sites from the first cycle five years later. This will provide direct data on real change in our forests, such as the increased rate of clear-felling, as well as assessing the impacts of climate change and the spread of pests and diseases. With this increasing change in woodlands comes a greater need to monitor and protect our woodlands and the Commission is using the latest satellite imagery, satellite radar data and artificial intelligence to detect felling, illegal felling, and the replanting of cut areas to ensure that Britain does not tip into deforestation. In 2016 the NFI used earth observation techniques to estimate Britain's first woodland loss statistics, which showed that Britain lost about 470 hectares of woodland per annum between 2006 and 2015 to urban development, even as Britain's overall woodland area expanded through new planting.

It is planned that further developments using the 'eye in the sky' will help the Commission to protect trees and woodland in Britain long into the future. One of the most striking research breakthroughs of 2018 was using artificial intelligence in combination with synthetic-aperture radar sensors mounted on satellites flying at almost 700 kilometres from earth to identify young trees only 20 centimetres tall. In future this technology could enable every restock site in Britain to be closely monitored in the seven years after felling to ensure that all clear-fell sites due for restocking are fully restocked. Such proof of concept projects offer exciting future possibilities for the operational use of earth observation to help protect and expand British woodlands.

# The Future

Over the last 100 years Britain's forest science has developed from a starting point of uncoordinated pockets of interest, through a phase of expansion focused largely around the practical needs of the growing forest industry, to today's capability which is multidisciplinary and broad in its objectives, partnerships and international interactions. The immediate focus is on protection (entomology, pathology, resilience and landscape-scale planning, management and restoration), adaptation to and mitigation of climate change (encompassing forest management options, species and genotype choice, an understanding of greenhouse gas fluxes and carbon budgets, the use of wood as a renewable energy resource and a substitute for high carbon and energy materials), management to limit the risk of flooding and fire, and advice on policy development which integrates current knowledge on biodiversity, social science, sustainability and ecosystem services. Technical developments, remote sensing, molecular biology, data handling, modelling, communications and foresight work have moved the delivery of forest science to previously unimagined levels.

The world's population and global economy continue to grow, placing greater demand on the availability of land and natural resources. The demand for wood-based products will grow to unprecedented levels over the coming decades against a background of declining global forest area. Not surprisingly given its role in conservation, recreation, sustainable development and climate mitigation, forestry features strongly in international science and conventions (e.g. in the Convention of Biological Diversity, Framework Convention on Climate Change, and the UN 2030 Agenda for Sustainable Development). The UK will need effective forest science as it deals with these issues domestically and internationally. Fortunately we have learnt a huge amount over the last 100 years, not only about forest science itself but also about trusting and encouraging scientific enquiry, and how to draw on broader science disciplines beyond pure forestry. A practical approach and commitment to the sector have been major themes in forestry research in Britain. Very significant progress has been made over the last 100 years; part of this can be attributed to those who understood what science could contribute and part to those who have delivered it. Many served to deliver forestry in line with the Forestry Commission's operational objectives both as forest scientists and as foresters and many were both excellent scientists and great colleagues.

# Appendix: List of Experiments

In listing the great British forestry experiments, those numbered by the Forestry Commission feature strongly. Any such listing will be a personal choice influenced by the time of compilation and the interests of the individual making the list. Some of the most important British forest experiments which continue to have an impact on forest science appear below.

| | |
|---|---|
| Blanche Benzian's experiments on nutrition in forest nurseries (Benzian 1965) | In early joint work involving Rothamsted Experimental Station and the Forestry Commission, Blanche Benzian used R. A. Fisher's Latin and Graeco-Latin square experiment designs and analysis of variance in Wareham Forest nursery. These classic experiments showed the importance of fertiliser use in forest nurseries and provided photographs from which nursery nutrient deficiencies could be identified. The experiments were beautifully designed and conducted and solved the practical issue of nursery nutrition. The Commission's forest gardens and arboreta are still the basis of our species-choice work today. |

| | |
|---|---|
| The Commission's forest gardens (*FC Bulletin* 12, 1931) | The Commission's forest gardens, some of which survive today as highly valued recreational and science sites, were intended as the second stage in the trial of species for use in woodlands and forests. In arboreta individuals of a large number of species are grown, while in the forest gardens species selected on the basis of their performance in the arboreta are grown in plots to trial for potential use in forestry right across the country. The surviving forest gardens are of high biodiversity and recreational value, and have also proved of considerable value as plot scale trials of tree species suitable for our changing climate. |
| The Ovington Plots (Ovington 1953, 1954, 1955 and 1957) | J. D. Ovington worked for the Nature Conservancy but also (as with R. A. Fisher and others at Rothamsted and elswhere) worked very closely with the Forestry Commission. His series of forest plots in Powis, Thetford Chase, the Forest of Dean, Bedgebury and later at other locations were classics of forest soil science, showing that tree stands have a major influence on the soils which develop beneath them. Generally forest floors beneath conifers are more acidic and have higher carbon but lower nitrogen content than those beneath hardwoods. There are also differences between the effects of different tree species on the soils beneath them. |
| The Permanent Sample plot network on which forest class system and yield models are based (Matthews et al. 2016) | The development at this time of yield models and the Yield Class system was one of the foundations of forest management and was a world first. The system, now available online and with considerable refinement (FC 2016), remains fundamentally as designed at that time and is still critical to forestry in Britain. |
| Frank Law's forest lysimeters in the Lake District | Frank Law worked for the Fylde Water Board and was the first person to set up large outdoor lysimeters to measure water flows beneath forest stands and in grassland systems. His early lysimeters (1954–70) were at Stocks Reservoir in the Forest of Bowland, Lancashire. Lysimeters of somewhat more modern design remain important equipment in forest and agricultural hydrology. With increasing drought and water availability concerns worldwide, this innovation must be considered as fundamentally important. |
| Beddgelert 12 (Kerr 2014) | A classic and elegant Forestry Commission silvicultural experiment, Beddgelert 12 was established in the 1950s–60s, illustrating the value of long-term joint work between the Forest District and Research. It showed which species were suitable in the very exposed British uplands and is described in more detail in Chapter 1 on Silviculture (see p. 99). |

| | |
|---|---|
| The Coalburn catchment (Nisbet 2005) | The Coalburn catchment (at the edge of Kielder Forest) is a long-running Forestry Commission trial of water use by conifers and of the consequential catchment water yield. Data from the experiment show how water use and the interception of mist by trees change as the stand develops. Like Gisburn 1 this is one of a number of Commission experiments which have been maintained into the second forest rotation – a rare but valuable achievement in forestry research globally. The management of water resources and flood control by landscape design continues to draw on the data being collected in the Coalburn catchment. |
| The Balquhidder catchment study | The Balquhidder catchment study has been run by the Institute of Hydrology and then the Centre for Ecology and Hydrology with Forestry Commission cooperation over many years. It followed on from Frank Law's pioneering work and is a comparison of the long-term hydrological consequences of different catchment management using the paired catchment approach. |
| Gisburn 1 (Mason and Connolly 2013) | A classic Forestry Commission silviculture trial, Gisburn 1 has shown the benefits of planting tree species in mixtures in the uplands (both species in two-species mixtures can grow better than either in pure species stands, but interactions are complex). |
| Tree Breeding Programme – progeny trials, seed orchards (Samuel, John & Lee 2000) | A major and ongoing tree breeding programme, this has produced improved genetic stock of both conifers and broadleaves for use in British forestry, e.g. improved Sitka spruce will yield 23 per cent more volume without loss of timber quality. Current and future work focuses on better disease and pest resistance and better adaptation to future climate. |
| Forest nutrition experiments (H. Miller 1981) | Classic forest nutrition research conducted by the Macaulay Land Use Research Institute and Aberdeen University with Forestry Commission cooperation, this work was important for a number of reasons, not least in that it showed that, provided forest stands were managed correctly, they could conserve nutrients as they grew and indeed even between rotations. Thus fertiliser use can be minimal (largely restricted to the first rotation establishment phase) so that nutrient run-off to ground and surface water (if it occurs at all) is much less than that from agricultural systems. |
| The Arboreta – Bedgebury and Westonbirt – and forest gardens – Kilmun (Mason et al. 1999), Brechfa etc. – trials | The arboreta trials show off individual or small groups of trees from across the world and are important for conservation, recreation and for first-stage selection of species for urban, garden, parkland and forest use. The Commission's forest gardens trial species which have shown promise for forestry use in the arboreta. Forest gardens need to be spread across the country (to trial different species x climate interactions) and need to have species plots to trial growth in stands which can be very different from growth as individual trees. |

CHAPTER 4

# Forest Hazards

*Threats to the Growing Forest – Storm,*
*Pestilence and Other Challenges*

Rebuilding Britain's forest resource through the 20th century meant that the foresters of the Forestry Commission had to learn about and adapt to a wide range of biological and environmental challenges. Many of these challenges were new – not least because of the prior loss of a tradition in forest management, but also because much of the new forest involved unfamiliar, newly introduced tree species on sites that had not borne trees for decades or even centuries. The novel combination of trees, sites and a maritime climate (rather than a continental climate, where much of the European expertise in forestry had developed) meant that some of these challenges were unexpected – and at times in the history of the Commission caused much concern. The challenges often combined chronic pressures with sporadic extreme events and outbreaks. Foresters learned to adapt to or avoid the chronic challenges using a range of techniques – underpinned by applied research – involving changes to site selection, species choice, felling age; alongside direct operations to counter threats (e.g. spraying against pests; fighting fires); and to respond to and accommodate the occasional severe event (e.g. using Task Forces to mobilise combined action across the public and private sectors). The challenges continue today – not least in the wave of introduced pests and diseases which are affecting our trees.

Vietnamese golden cypress *(Xanthocyparis vietnamensis)*

# Hazards

The early Forestry Commission was pioneering the reafforestation of the UK and learning to manage new woodlands. The novelty of the undertaking and the lack of substantial areas of woodland to observe and from which to learn, meant that there was little understanding of the threats which might be encountered. The lack of established wisdom, or culture of woodland management, meant that there was little to draw upon when assessing what might frustrate the establishment and growth of the new trees.

This lack of observable role model was compounded by the very considerable variety of environmental conditions, particularly climate and soil, encountered across the land upon which the new forests were established. It might be at least 50 (and perhaps as much as 150) years before the trees were ready for harvest, enough time for rare extreme events to happen and new threats to emerge.

Although instinctively we might understand what constitutes a threat, it is hard to establish a single definition. Threats may include events and processes that impact upon the very survival or some key and valued characteristic of trees, woods and forests. In the case of the existential threats (leading to loss and death of trees), perhaps there is less scope for ambiguity or disagreement. However, some other threats, as we will see in due course, depend upon an interpretation of largely natural processes; in particular, the extent to which they prevent particular goals, merely act as an inconvenience or complication, or bring new opportunities. In essence, one tree's disaster might be another's renewal.

In broad terms, there are four types of response which managers can take to address perceived threats. The preferred response, what is deemed acceptable, and what seems to be worthwhile have changed over the decades. Each of these response types can be observed in the practice of British forestry of the past 100 years.

## Types of Response to Threats

**Resistance** – actions which directly confront the threat and seek to reduce it at source; e.g. killing the pest/disease organism which threatens the trees.

**Adaptation** – altering plans, aspects of the overall endeavour, to make the threat less likely or less impactful; e.g. changes to forest structure to reduce the risk of fire during drought.

**Recovery** – focusing on plans to recover in the aftermath of an event – where the likelihood or timing of this is very uncertain or not susceptible to resistance/adaptation actions; e.g. plans to recover from catastrophic wind storms.

**Transformation** – reassessment of level of threat or nature of impact which may lead to decisions to pursue completely different courses of action or enterprise; e.g. opting not to replant sites which proved to be too exposed/wet/nutrient poor for adequate growth of trees.

# The Different Threats to Trees in Britain

There are at least five characteristics which might help profile a threat and determine the appropriate response. Firstly, what is its *origin* – is it climatic (e.g. ice, snow, wind, drought), is it biological (e.g. involving other organisms which feed on the trees or attack them in some other way), is it related to human activities (e.g. air pollution affecting the health of foliage), or are there several factors acting together in synergy as a complex and compound threat (e.g. drought leading to stressed trees more susceptible to insect attack)? Secondly, the profiling might consider *when* the threat might manifest itself: does it apply only when trees are young or old (clearly of importance if foresters are learning as we go), or at any stage in the life of the trees? Thirdly, the profiling could consider the *duration* of the threat: is it sudden and dramatic (e.g. the storm of October 1987 in south-east England), or slow and gradual (e.g. shifts in precipitation patterns with climate change)? Fourthly, is the *spatial extent* of the threat such that it affects only a single locality (e.g. the 2012 outbreak of Asian longhorn beetle in the vicinity of Paddock Wood) or widely experienced across large regions or the whole country (e.g. the emerging outbreak of ash dieback)? Finally, the profiling might consider the *impact* of the threat: is the result damage to parts of trees (e.g. browsing of leading shoots by deer) or the death of many trees (e.g. in a disease outbreak of *Phytophthora ramorum* in larch)? How does the impact challenge what the forester had planned – whether the production of quality timber, a contribution to a wooded landscape, the perpetuation of a woodland habitat, or the provision of a wooded space for recreation?

Trees are long-lived organisms which have evolved to face many challenges through adaptation and inherent resilience. Rather like humans, their susceptibilities change with age: a threat in young age may not be a threat in old age – and vice versa. The art of the forester has been to understand and work with these characteristics – while coping with the episodic nature of some of the threats, and the long-term changes in the extent and sensitivity of the forests to such threats.

# Climatic Threats

Although Britain's maritime climate is generally very suitable for growing trees, providing long growing seasons with adequate moisture and reasonable warmth for a wide range of temperate trees, there are nevertheless threats associated with it.

## Drought and Fire

In some years, lack of rain causes drought – and some tree species, sites and regions are more prone than others. Drought years (such as 1976, 1994/95, 2003 and 2018) impact on the growth of trees and are often marked by a narrow growth ring in the stem wood. They may cause increased mortality of trees on the driest sites, and may be associated with an increase in summer fires started accidentally. Droughts are forecast to increase in frequency with climate change, especially in the east of Britain, and this is now leading foresters to reconsider which tree species should be used. Some species are much more prone than others to mortality when experiencing drought, so adapting to this enhanced threat should lead, for example, to more cautious use of beech in south-east England and Sitka spruce in east Scotland.

Although fires are more frequent in drought years, the threat is modest compared with that experienced in more continental or Mediterranean climates where intense dry periods and high temperatures can result in fires becoming life-threatening for humans and newsworthy (e.g. recent dramatic footage from Spain, Portugal and Scandinavia). Although summer droughts may become more common in the coming years, until now the more pervasive threat of fire in UK forests has not been due to extreme drought years but to the annual cycle of vegetation growth in upland areas. The fire season dominated the daily life of many Forestry Commission staff from February to May as the seasonal dry spell coincided with the presence of dead and dry vegetation on moorlands and heathlands close to or around the newly planted young trees, and adjacent to established woodland. The practice of deliberate muirburning to obtain fresh vegetation for sheep or grouse, sparks from steam engines or the wheels of diesel trains, a carelessly discarded cigarette butt or untended campfires were all potential ignition sources from which fires could rapidly develop. To counter and resist this threat was the focus of much activity and innovation. Squads were trained, equipment to deliver water or foam developed, fire traces were swiped, lookouts organised, staff rostered, signs erected, fire services involved, and helicopters deployed.

## The Fire Season

The fire season dominated the spring activities of many Forestry Commission staff.

*In preparation:*
- Fire traces were swiped to reduce flammable vegetation near to high-risk roads and rail tracks;
- Equipment was prepared – fire beaters were made and displayed around forests;
- Signs were erected and information disseminated around campsites and visitor centres, and regularly emphasised in the Commission's publications;
- Staff were trained (e.g. latterly in safely entering and exiting helicopters while carrying fire beaters or knapsack sprayers);
- Liaison was undertaken with neighbours (e.g. to establish their plans for muirburning) and with emergency services (including local military bases).

*On each day in the season:*
- Weather observations were taken at the local Commission office (these readings contributed a major part of the Met Office's climate network in upland/rural Britain before the advent of automated weather stations);
- Ratings were used to establish fire risk and the result broadcast over radio networks to all the Commission's staff in the area: if the scores were high, then lookouts (often in fire towers) and vehicle patrols were deployed, and squads were kept on standby.

*If fires were spotted:*
- The level of threat was established;
- Squads and machinery were mobilised (beaters, bowsers, foam-laying units, helicopters). Partner organisations were called upon to help;
- If likely to require many hours of firefighting, catering was organised and shift rosters established.

*After fire:*
- The hot spots were damped down to avoid the fire flaring up again;
- Investigations and enquiries were carried out;
- Loss reports were made and lessons learnt.

Arson was also a recurrent threat in some regions, notably south Wales, south-west Scotland and north-east England. In these areas special measures were taken to reduce the threat by additional efforts to remove flammable verge-side vegetation, increasing patrols, maintaining helicopters 'on call', and particular efforts to engage with local communities to dissuade arsonists. For a time, when the rapid afforestation after the Second World War meant there was a very large area of young forest with flammable ground cover in these regions, the threat was so frequent that management structures and district boundaries were changed to focus on the task of reducing fire starts and develop expertise in a particular group of staff. Even today, when the extent of the flammable ground cover has reduced as the forests have matured, fire remains a serious concern for those charged with managing British forests and likely to remain so given the forecast changes to our climate. In the Forestry Commission, weather monitoring, contingency planning, vegetation management, warnings to visitors, and staff training all form part of the toolkit to control this particular threat.

## Wetness

An excess of moisture has been more of a challenge on many of the sites which foresters have sought to use. In particular a combination of high rainfall, low permeability of soils, and lack of slope to encourage run-off, has meant that many upland soils experience seasonal waterlogging; in most winter months the water table gets very close to the ground surface. Tree roots of many species do not cope well with the resultant anaerobic conditions and active growing tips can be repeatedly killed off; this prevents deep rooting and leads to a shallow and flat root system with characteristic 'shaving brush' clusters of roots. Such shallow root systems render trees vulnerable to toppling in strong winds (discussed below) and can be associated with land slips on steeper slopes.

Reducing the waterlogging to enhance root depth became a major endeavour and a preoccupation of researchers and practitioners through the mid-20th century. A wide variety of techniques was tested and developed to provide raised planting sites and increase the rate of drainage of sites. These ranged from the ingenious (mole ploughs which extruded a ribbon of peat and left a channel clear underground), to the bold (attempting to plough sites bearing stumps from the previous rotation by sheer brute power using a Caterpillar D7 tractor), to the hazardous (some limited trials of explosives as a ditch forming technique) and the pragmatic (deploying excavators modified from those used in civil engineering to mound soil into discrete planting spots). This pursuit of the technological fix in itself provides rich material for epic stories of failed attempts to plough very steep or very wet sites, mass 'boggings' of machinery, and the particular contribution of the ploughing tractor driver to forestry culture (these particularly well-informed individuals took news and gossip from forest to forest as they travelled between sites, and were often the first to announce a staff transfer between units). This approach to site preparation has now been replaced with a more proportionate and adaptive one: accepting that the wettest sites should not be ploughed or planted, being mindful of downstream consequences and so taking care to prevent silt from entering watercourses, choosing the appropriate species for the site conditions, and using modest amounts of equipment to prepare the site rather than attempting wholesale domination of sites.

## Wind

The climatic threat with the biggest impact on the style of forestry practised by the Forestry Commission and on the thinking behind it, has undoubtedly been wind. The British Isles are extremely windy compared with many other forested areas of the world – and particularly in comparison with areas of central Europe where much forest practice developed prior to the formation of the Commission. In particular, in the north and west of Britain, the wind-speeds are perhaps rivalled only by those in south-east Alaska and southern Chile (or inhospitable areas close to the poles or at very high elevation in mountainous regions). The sustained windiness impacts the growth and survival of trees, and has dominated species choice – restricting it to a very small number of exposure-tolerant species on the windiest sites. Growth rate and elevational limits to planting are affected as much by windiness as temperature, whereas in many continental areas, temperature alone prescribes where the tree line will be found.

How this windiness varied over the new lands made available for afforestation was not well understood in the first half of the 20th century, even by professional meteorologists and climatologists. Forestry Commission researchers developed a unique understanding of it. In particular, the use of cotton flags (so-called tatter flags) was developed to indicate windiness. This simple technique allowed monitoring of many hundreds of sites for research and latterly to directly indicate the boundaries of land suitable for planting. In time, the accumulated results were pooled and used to develop a predictive system to estimate general windiness and the frequency of the strongest winds capable of damaging mature trees.

## The Use of Tatter Flags to Measure Windiness

The tatter flag was used before modern battery-operated weather stations were developed and became affordable. The idea came from an advisory visit to Orkney by a member of Forest Research, John Zehetmayr, in the early 1950s. He heard a story about a sea captain who had placed a set of flags across his estate as a way of identifying the most sheltered site for his new house – the preferred site being the one where the least material was lost over the time during which the flags were flown. This simple notion was tested, refined and standardised with respect to the material used (Madapollam cloth of a standard weave – apparently the same as was used to clad gliders in the Second World War but without the rot-proofing), length of exposure, height and method of flag mounting.

Flags were changed every two months and a three-year run was found to provide sufficient precision for reliable estimation of planting limits. The flags were also used to characterise the windiness of many silvicultural experiment sites, and the accumulated records were in time summarised in modern decision support systems which predicted the growth rate of trees (Ecological Site Classification) and the likelihood of wind damage (the Windthrow Hazard Classification and the successor ForestGALES). Some flags even found their way as far afield as New Zealand, the Falklands and Everest!

Wind damage to mature trees through overturning or snap of the main stem (together termed 'windthrow') was not a threat which received much attention in the early years of the Forestry Commission (unlike the effects of chronic windiness and salt-laden winds on young trees which were rapidly understood to be a constraint on planting ambitions and choice of species). Yet windthrow came to dominate much silvicultural practice and forest planning in the uplands during the second half of the 20th century. Although historical records suggest strong winds have caused windthrow repeatedly over the centuries (there are certainly records from the 13th century and signs of fallen trees in peat deposits exposed along the Bristol Channel), the magnitude of the constraint may not have been recognised because of the very lack of mature woodland in Britain and the lack of contemporary experience – or perhaps it had been forgotten in the rush to afforest? Inklings of the magnitude of the problem surfaced in the 1950s; for example, an account in *The Journal of the Forestry Commission* in 1951 by S. M. Petrie, entitled 'Gale Warning! Windblow in Western Spruce Plantations', spoke of the shock of early damage to woodlands and raised concerns about future events.

The threat was reinforced by catastrophic storm damage in January 1953 in north-east Scotland (the same storm event which caused widespread flooding in east England and the Low Countries) during which millions of trees (representing approximately 1.8 million cubic metres of timber) were windthrown – possibly a quarter or a third of the semi-mature and mature trees in the region which had survived the wartime felling of the previous decade. Forestry Commission accounts at the time provide graphic descriptions of the aftermath:

It has been remarked that it is as if a giant searchlight had been turned on to the countryside knocking down all it illuminated . . .

Meanwhile the forests present a sad sight and are very vulnerable to fires and plagues of rabbits and insects. Owners' schemes for the systematic management of their woods have been severely upset.

While the initial focus was on clearance and recovery – and support to the many private owners affected – attention started to be paid to how greater stability (e.g. through the achievement of deeper rooting) might be gained. Another major windthrow event, in January 1968, struck at the core of the new spruce forests in west and central Scotland, affecting some of the most productive woodlands and again removing at least a quarter of the growing stock. In January 1976 it was the turn of Wales, the Midlands and East Anglia to be affected – and then in October 1987, unusually, the south and east of England experienced hurricane-force winds. In each case, mobilisation of machinery and labour, prioritisation of clearance, coordination of marketing, and assistance in the form of advice and financial assistance was necessary to aid the recovery of the Forestry Commission and private woodlands. Methods were developed to prevent staining and fungal degrade of timber once felled by storing under sprinkler systems until the wood-using industries were ready for it.

However, in the uplands it became apparent that it was not these rare events which were the main challenge but the frequent storms experienced in most winters; these exposed weak spots in the forest and punished poor silvicultural practice such as delayed and late thinning. The search for improved tree stability not only considered improved rooting depth (through site drainage or disruption of indurated soil layers), but also looked for species differences in ability to root deeply, and recognised the importance of thinning patterns and timing, and felling sequences and forest layout, as being influential and meriting attention. The magnitude of the threat for a time came to dominate much of silvicultural practice in the uplands.

Researchers experimented on a grand scale (cutting circular holes of a range of sizes in Ae Forest), used topographic models (and latterly scaled tree models) in wind tunnels, deployed sophisticated instruments, and were early adopters of geographic information systems (GIS) in a quest to understand the problem and help develop adaptive solutions. The knowledge was codified initially in a Windthrow Hazard Classification and latterly in a computer-based decision support system, ForestGALES (which incidentally has now been adapted for use in Canada, New Zealand, France and Japan). As a result, some of the riskier practices were eliminated and the management of upland forests adapted to and accommodated this threat to an extent which is perhaps world-leading. Strong winds continue to challenge foresters in their planning and management: anticipating the threat, adapting plans to minimise damage, developing contingency plans, and mobilising resources should the worst happen have become engrained in practice. The impact of climate change on the frequency of storms remains a cause for concern and continued attention.

## The Storm of October 1987

The storm of 16 October 1987 was a reminder of how windy Britain can be but it was a major surprise in the part of the country which was affected. The winds were so strong as likely to be experienced, on average, only every 200 years or so in south-east England (though more frequently in the north and west – perhaps every 50 years or so in west Scotland). Rather like the 1953 storm, the woodlands affected were largely in private ownership and so the role of the Forestry Commission was typically to support, survey, coordinate and grant aid to the efforts to recover and replant.

With hindsight, the initial reactions of horror and disaster have been replaced by the recognition that some of the change has been a positive opportunity: for new landscapes, for more diverse structured woodlands, and for those plant and animal species that benefit from light reaching the forest floor to thrive rather than struggle in the closed canopy woodland which was coming to dominate the region.

## Frost and Snow

Two further climatic threats deserve brief mention for the challenge which they have provided to British foresters.

Firstly, as many gardeners know, frost in late spring or early autumn can be a damaging problem and can lead to death of young trees. Although it is directly associated with particular weather patterns, some locations both regionally (away from the coast) and locally (e.g. topographies leading to 'frost hollows') can be particularly prone to recurrent frosts. Species choice (and to some extent provenance choice – which affects the timing of bud burst and set) has been key to accommodating this threat. As we seek new species to suit the new warmer climates that are forecast for later in the century, the occurrence of frost and occasional very low winter temperatures as a sporadic constraint cannot be ignored. For example, the winter of 2009–10 led to dramatic losses in biomass trials in Cumbria of two newly planted eucalyptus species; temperatures of −14°C caused almost 99 per cent mortality in *Eucalyptus nitens* by spring of the following year.

Secondly, heavy falls of snow (and very rarely of freezing rain) can cause localised problems, leading to branch breakage and crown loss which can spoil vistas and provide entrance wounds for decay fungi. Some locations seem particularly prone (e.g. woods on the North York Moors) but even areas such as the New Forest can be affected. There is a colourful account in *The Journal of the Forestry Commission* of 1938:

> The New Forest ... gained unwanted notoriety last December from a snowstorm – a blizzard the press called it. Strictly speaking, a blizzard is accompanied by wind; this snow fell on a perfectly windless night ...

> About 9 o'clock the real damage began, then the noise became continuous. My house has woods at the back and trees all round, so I had good opportunity to hear it. First one branch would go with the noise that a tree makes when it has felled and crashes to the ground. Before that had finished, one, two and even four or five would follow in a crescendo of noise and an unwonted absence of echo. Dead silence would follow and then the noise would begin again and might be protracted for five or ten minutes with scarcely a break

The relative rarity and unpredictability of such events mean that snow is largely considered an occasional inconvenience and part of the suite of natural processes that have to be accommodated, rather than anything meriting change in practice.

# Anthropogenic Threats

Some of the most serious threats to the survival and health of the establishing forests have been anthropogenic in origin. Chief among these are the extent of wartime felling, the loss of woods to transport infrastructure and building development, and the fluctuating nature of political support and public funding for planting and management of trees. Pollution has also been a problem; for example, widespread ecosystem disturbance due to acid rain; localised effects due to fluoride and other heavy metals from smelters, ammonia emissions from agriculture, and a range of chemicals from vehicles' exhaust fumes. There are concerns that such avoidable threats contribute to loss of condition in trees and may predispose them to attack by pests and diseases.

# Pests and Diseases

Pests and diseases constitute the class of threat which is currently uppermost in the minds of many foresters. That is not to say that insects and fungi have not been regarded as a threat throughout the life of the Forestry Commission – indeed some shaped the early species choice (e.g. provenances of larch, European silver fir). However, much of the early adaptation involved accommodating the effects of a limited number of endemic pests and diseases, and learning how they might impact the new tree species being used in afforestation. The contemporary problem is more complex and involves learning to cope with the impacts and uncertainty caused by the changing behaviour in endemic species associated with climate change, together with the unwitting introduction of new pests and diseases from around the world. These organisms are hitch-hiking across the world as a by-product of increased (and rapid) trade in a range of products including live plants (with whole soil ecosystems), and wood or wood packaging (e.g. pallets and frames to transport machinery, slate and ceramics). The threat may be compounded by centralisation of production and supply which may aid the subsequent dispersal of diseased material. Alarmingly, some of these organisms are of no threat in their native conditions – and may have co-evolved with very different tree species – but may have greater impacts in novel situations presented by their arrival. There is also the worrying prospect of hybridisation of existing species leading to the creation of new pathogens.

## What Constitutes a Disease or Pest?

Diseases of trees are caused by a wide range of organisms – chiefly fungi but also oomycetes, viruses and bacteria. Pests are typically thought of as insects (including bark beetles, aphids, weevils, and larvae of sawflies and moths) which affect or consume roots, stem, cambium, wood or foliage at stages in their developmental cycles. Pest status is sometimes afforded to a wider range of organisms from nematodes to vertebrate animals – notably deer, rabbits, hares, voles, squirrels (especially the introduced North American grey squirrel), goats and domestic animals. Indeed when, in the early years of the Forestry Commission, there was an absolute focus on timber production and the growth of straight-stemmed trees (which were easiest to use in mills etc.), an even wider range of wildlife was considered a threat – including some now treasured and rare species such as the red squirrel, capercaillie and black grouse, and other more commonplace ones such as the starling (where large roosts of birds were seen as problematic and damaging).

Each pest or disease has a particular mode of attack which provides a particular challenge to tree defences, and impacts upon particular functions of the tree and particular parts – whether roots, stem, bark or foliage (or some combination of these). The impact may be manifest in a variety of ways and cause a range of problems from disfigurement and reduced growth rate to mortality of individual or whole groups of trees.

## Classifying Pests and Diseases

There are many different ways of classifying these threats. Confusingly the statutory position until very recently called all pests and diseases 'pests'! It is possible to distinguish them by biology, e.g. pests and diseases; occurrence, e.g. on trees of young age versus old age; taxonomic types, e.g. scientific names; nativeness, e.g. endemic or exotic; tree host (which can also be by taxonomic type or by nativeness); or impacts on trees, e.g. survival, condition, specific qualities.

Pests can be separated into broad biological groupings of bark beetles, weevils and wood borers (causing girdling, damage to timber value, transmission of fungal pathogens); aphids, scale insects and other sucking invertebrates (causing impacts on foliage and tree condition, and possibly transmitting diseases such as bacteria and viruses); and lepidoptera and sawflies (causing extensive defoliation).

Pathogens can be separated into broad groupings of foliar pathogens; root pathogens and rots; stem cankers; stress-related/ latent; and other – including wilts and bluestains.

Foresters have developed a number of strategies, and in some cases ingenious and innovative methods, to overcome the threat or at least moderate the worst of the impacts. These include avoiding the problem by control of movement of timber/infected trees, good hygiene at nurseries, and general biosecurity; choice of tree species to avoid particularly susceptible types; matching tree species to site conditions and thereby minimising physiological stresses which might be a precursor (or render the tree more vulnerable) to attack by pests and diseases; development of pre-planting or prophylactic treatment, using a range of insecticides; treatment of cut stumps to prevent colonisation by harmful fungi (see Box on *Fomes annosus*); barrier methods using shelters, guards and fences against vertebrate pests (and in the case of guards as barriers against weevils (see Box on *Hylobius abietis*); chemical control treatments – a wide range over the years but now fewer in number and more restricted in use due to environmental concerns (partly also met by greater specificity and localised treatment); and biological control by deploying predators, parasites, nematodes or bacteria to reduce populations of the problem organism.

## *Fomes annosus* (*Heterobasidion annosum*)

This fungus is an endemic disease largely controlled/kept at bay by consistent management using tried and tested methods. It is associated with butt rot affecting the most valuable part (for timber) of conifer trees of a wide range of species. Entry of the fungus is via wounds on the stem or through root contacts with infected material (such as standing trees or colonised stumps), and so is particularly a threat when the site has already had trees and is being replanted. Many of the 20th-century new forests were established on sites without trees and therefore had initially no substantial inoculum. However, the spores are ubiquitous and able to colonise freshly cut stumps resulting from thinning or clear-felling operations.

By altering the properties of the cut surfaces of stumps so that they are no longer receptive to colonisation by the pathogen (using an application of urea), or introducing a competing decay fungus which is no threat to living trees (using *Peniophora*), it has been possible to prevent the widespread establishment of the disease in the new forests. Measures are increasingly targeted to sites where the potential for disease development is high, due to both climate and soil type. In special cases, such as Thetford Forest, wholesale stump removal has contributed to reducing the risk of mortality in the next rotation but this is costly and only possible where there is deep sandy soil.

## *Hylobius abietis*, the Large Pine Weevil

This is a pest with a long history as a troublemaker which remains a challenge. It is an endemic pest of conifer forests, affecting a wide range of tree species (despite the name). Feeding adult weevils can cause widespread damage to and death of young trees, particularly on replanting sites (restocking sites which have already borne trees). The eggs are laid around the stump and roots of mature trees within which the immature stages then develop. Upon emergence the adults start feeding on nearby plants – the damage is primarily by girdling the stems and branches of young trees leading to shoot and stem death.

A number of insecticide treatments have been developed to protect plants, including innovative methods developed in Forestry Commission nurseries to apply them in a targeted and low dosage manner. However, with enhanced environmental regulation, fewer insecticides are now available. As felling programmes increase in upland forests with the maturing of the post-war plantings, and in some areas through sanitation felling to reduce the risk of *Dothistroma* needle blight, conditions have been created for high density populations to develop as a result of the wealth of breeding materials.

The threat is currently mitigated by pre-treatment of plants in the nursery, top-up sprays on restocking sites, use of nematodes to reduce the weevil population, or fallow periods so that replanting takes place after the peak weevil population has passed. A computer-based management support system helps guide foresters in choice of method. In future, new methods are likely to involve a move towards integrated pest management and greater reliance on biological control methods (such as entomopathogenic fungi), as well as greater attention to forest design to avoid the build-up of high-density populations.

Forestry has learnt to live with a number of the long-established pests and diseases by moderating its worst effects using a selection of the range of methods above; research and development continues to seek alternatives and refine methods. There have been some notable successes (e.g. *Fomes annosus*), and the use of a predator *Rhizophagus grandis* to control the spread of *Dendroctonus micans*; some for which achieving an appropriate equilibrium/accommodation is best considered 'work in progress', including where the solutions are perhaps known but the trade-offs are seen as unacceptable (e.g. *Hylobius abietis*); and others where success cannot yet be claimed except perhaps in a small number of localities where coordinated action has been achieved (e.g. grey squirrels).

## Grey Squirrels

Grey squirrels were introduced from the eastern half of North America from the 1870s and rapidly escaped from the estates into which they had been introduced. An awareness of the problem of their expanding populations emerged in the late 1940s as management attention focused on the rehabilitation of broadleaved woodland and with the realisation that they strip the bark from many broadleaved tree species. This stripping substantially reduces the value of the trees, and can lead to mortality. In addition, the grey squirrels have displaced the native red squirrel across much of its former range through competition for food and spreading of disease. Grey squirrels are now widespread across England, Wales and southern and eastern Scotland. The development of humane control methods was successful but application was costly and time-consuming – as well as frustrating if efforts were rendered useless by reintroduction from neighbouring woodlands. UK foresters still cite grey squirrels as one of their major problems today. In recent years there has been interest in developing immune-contraception methods and an indication that reintroducing our native pine marten might shift populations back in favour of red squirrels.

A distinct concern, and perhaps a deeper systemic threat, is the establishment of new pests and diseases, including those not yet seen in these islands, for which methods are not available, and whose impacts are unpredictable and potentially grievous. In the past decade, a notable upswing in concern has been expressed around newly introduced or uncovered pests and diseases which have started to exert significant impacts on tree health. While such introductions are not necessarily a new phenomenon, there seems to have been a worrying trend in increased rate of discovery which cannot be explained as just the impact of better detection methods (e.g. molecular diagnostics, which itself bring challenges of interpretation). Although regulation of movement of some hazardous materials, requirements for phytosanitary certificates, and border control (e.g. port inspections of consignments of wood, timber and plants) seek to maintain biosecurity, the volume and rapidity of trade is a major challenge. Interception of unwanted organisms or infected plants does lead to destruction of consignments but only a small sample are routinely inspected, many may have cryptic phases when detection is particularly difficult, and some are not even recognised as posing a risk until they encounter a naïve host. Some biosecurity measures are now being taken overseas so that infected materials are not transported, and some regulations have developed to prevent obvious pathways (e.g. heat treatment of wood pallets to prevent spread of harmful nematodes).

Once within the UK (when borders are breached), early detection and eradication are clearly desirable. There have been some successes, most notably the apparently successful eradication of the Asian longhorn beetle in the Paddock Wood area. In autumn 2018 another unwanted beetle (*Ips typographus*) was detected in routine protected zone surveys: intensive efforts are underway to eradicate this too. There has also been greater attention to those organisms yet to arrive and which are already understood to be a threat based on knowledge of their home range or the experiences from other countries in which they have been introduced. The UK Plant Health Risk Register provides a comprehensive listing of such threats (current undesirables include plane wilt, *Xylella*, and the emerald ash borer).

## Asian Longhorn Beetle (ALB)

Grubs of the Asian longhorn beetle develop in conditions in the UK over a period of two to three years in the live woody tissues (stems/branches/roots) of a wide range of broadleaved trees and can cause considerable damage/death by their feeding activities. They may be undetectable until emergence – at which point the large exit hole may become apparent.

An outbreak of ALB was discovered in March 2012 in the Paddock Wood area. The arrival was uncovered when a member of the public spotted a large and unusual beetle crossing their driveway. Identification and signs in the vicinity were confirmed by Forest Research and Defra staff. Prior assessment of the potential for damage should it become established, prompted rapid action. The outbreak was centred on a former stone importer's yard and a control/eradication zone was set up around it, with the felling of all possible host trees in the vicinity and precautionary felling of further host trees in a buffer zone of 2 kilometres beyond the outermost infected trees. In all, 2,166 trees were felled over a period of a few weeks. The site was inspected annually until 2018; after five years, it is possible to declare that eradication is a success if no further signs are detected (i.e. insects or new exit holes). In this case, there was successful eradication of an unwanted new arrival.

Unfortunately, not all organisms are stopped from entering or detected early enough to enable eradication. These then pose a fresh challenge of attempting to control spread and assess what can be done to restrict the outbreak and mitigate the impacts. The most notable example in recent years has been ash dieback – but oak processionary moth and *Phytophthora ramorum* (killing larch in western Britain) have also caused substantial problems. In each case, these organisms have been introduced unwittingly through trade (and in the case of ash dieback, also by airborne spread from the Continent) and now pose a serious threat to trees and woods. Oak processionary moth (OPM) was first detected in 2005/06 and has now become established in the London area despite extensive control efforts including spraying of individual trees and manual nest removal. In addition to the weakening of host oak trees through defoliation by the OPM caterpillars, contact with the hairs on the caterpillars can cause irritation and in some cases severe human health impacts. The case of *Phytophthora ramorum* is particularly alarming as it had previously been assessed as a possible threat to oak and several shrub species (including vaccinium and rhododendron) and so the jump to killing larch was a complete surprise. This emphasises the unpredictability resulting from novel combinations of pathogen and host; as one Forestry Research scientist noted, these are 'uncontrolled experiments in evolution'.

## Ash Dieback

Ash dieback (due to the fungus *Hymenoscyphus fraxineus*) was first detected in the UK in 2012, though subsequent investigations suggest that it arrived some time before. Its arrival via both trade in plants and as airborne spores has been indicated by different lines of evidence and it is unlikely that we will ever know which of these mechanisms represented its initial mode of introduction. An initial flurry of activity prompted by media interest and political concern (including a Cabinet Office Briefing Room, or COBR, meeting – the government's highest level emergency response committee – to which Forestry Commission officials were summoned) resulted in rapid mobilisation of Forestry Commission personnel and other tree professionals to try to establish the extent of the problem before autumn leaf fall made this impractical. However, it was soon apparent that the scale of the outbreak was already such that eradication was not possible. The focus has therefore been on slowing the spread, encouraging adaptation (e.g. through identification of tolerant ash trees, genetic research and greater use of natural regeneration), and enhanced biosecurity to avoid other undesirable organisms following similar pathways.

In the face of such threats (and further uncertainties over trade and how it might change following the UK's projected exit from the EU), there has been renewed attention to biosecurity – pre-border, at the border, and within the border (e.g. the 'Keep it clean' campaigns and Protected Zone surveys) – and prior preparedness (e.g. in contingency planning). There has also been an emphasis on improving the chances of early warning (e.g. helicopter surveys, exploration of remote-sensing capabilities, and traps and sentinel trees near major ports and trade hubs). Recently, there has been success in encouraging wider participation in the search for unwanted organisms, by encouraging citizen scientists to keep an eye on the health of trees and woodlands which they visit. The Observatree project, a partnership of nine organisations, has trained more than 200 volunteers to look out for pests and diseases. Their mobilisation has been supplemented by a range of training and survey materials, and the development of a web-based portal (TreeAlert) to aid quality reporting. They have logged thousands of records, including several notable observations giving early warning of range spread.

As long-lived organisms, trees have adapted to withstand a

remarkably wide range of fluctuations in the growing conditions and climate which they experience. Our oldest trees have accommodated at least 1,000 years of change – ten times the history of the Forestry Commission! However, those responsible for management (and stewardship) of such precious assets cannot afford to be complacent and just rely on the inherent resilience of the trees. Over the past 100 years the Forestry Commissioners and its foresters have wrestled with a variety of threats to the trees, woods and forests for which they have been responsible. Some threats were perhaps mirages and the product of a single-minded pursuit of timber as the only goal; the measures taken have long since been superseded (e.g. stamping on capercaillie nests to control the population and prevent damage to leading shoots of pine trees). Others, though considerable and enduring, have been the focus of significant learning and the development of adaptive management (e.g. *Fomes annosus* and strong winds). Some remain a live issue and source of contemporary effort (e.g. many pests and diseases recently introduced) for which a positive outcome is by no means assured, though efforts will continue. Others remain a future potential threat, prompting the need for preparatory action (e.g. responding to climate change forecasts through matching of tree species to site and region). Finally, some remain unknown with the worrying prospect of novel combinations of pest/disease and host trees, or combined synergistic effects of several threats, causing surprises. This underlines the need for continued vigilance.

# CHAPTER 5

# The Arts in the Forest

Over the last 50 years, among the trees and woods managed by the Forestry Commission, hundreds of artists have been involved in creating, presenting and engaging audiences with artworks in every imaginable form, from sculpture and sound to film and festivals, architecture and archives to literature and theatre. Only a selection of these projects can be explored here and our focus is on those that have made the most significant contribution to how forest art works and has developed. Many of these projects have won significant accolades and awards. None would have been possible without the vital contributions of the many partners, collaborators, curators, communities, creative practitioners, forestry staff, funders, stakeholders and supporters involved in this area of the Forestry Commission's work which is unquestionably a subject worthy of a fuller record in the future.

# Origins

## Theatre and Sculpture in the Forest: Grizedale

It all started at Grizedale Forest in the Lake District. Acquired by the Forestry Commission in 1937 from the Brocklebank Family of Cunard Shipping fame, the estate buildings became home to the Theatre in the Forest, which was founded in 1968. The only theatre in the whole area at that time, it was housed in a converted hayloft at the visitor centre. Formerly the space had been used for public talks and events about countryside and forest management. The hayloft was converted into a professional 230-seat auditorium and hosted a wide range of music including classical, folk and jazz, as well as drama, ballet, natural history events and films – all run with the support of volunteers. During the 31 years of its existence (it closed in 1999 after other theatres were established in the area), the Theatre in the Forest played host to many renowned performers, including John Lill, Annie Fischer, John Ogdon, Kenny Ball, the Northern Sinfonia of England, Ken Dodd and Pam Ayres, along with a range of established theatre companies.

This pioneering work was led by the Forestry Commission's South Lakes District Officer Martin Orram and delivered with his Chief Forester Bill Grant; it grew out of other advances made there in the 1960s. In 1960 Orram's boss came back from the Commonwealth Forestry Conference and brought back the first Nature Trail interpretation that anyone had ever seen in Britain. Orram quickly set to work creating the first interpretative map and guide available to visitors, a booklet interpreting the Riding Wood area of the forest which is still an important accessible walking trail in Grizedale today.

This development was soon followed by the creation of car parks on Coniston Water's eastern shore along the western edge of Grizedale Forest. At the Visitor Centre the training centre that had been created for Wildlife Rangers was opened to the public. The available buildings were converted from the estate of Grizedale Hall and housed an innovative Deer Interpretation Centre, showcasing the history of the forest's deer population, which includes the only remaining indigenous red deer herd in the country. Bill Grant then built 'Treetops' and various small hides around the forest for watching deer which were booked for overnight stays by the public. These innovations gradually introduced people to the forest and were early pilots of the recreational facilities and opportunities offered across the country today.

The Theatre in the Forest had quickly developed a significant reputation, dedicated audience and the community infrastructure to run the venue. So when Peter Davies, then Arts Officer at Northern Arts, was exploring the region in search of a suitable base for an artist-in-residence programme, Grizedale Forest was an ideal location. It offered the necessary space, support and materials as well as plentiful inspiration in a diverse and well-established forest landscape in the Lake District. Davies and Northern Arts provided the financial and curatorial support to get the project off the ground and the founding of the programme in 1977 secured Grizedale Forest's reputation as the UK's first forest for sculpture.

The history of 20th-century British sculpture and its connection with landscape provided significant art-historical context. Henry Moore created works responding to the landscape of his studio's location in Much Hadham and Barbara Hepworth's relationship with the Cornish coast surrounding her studio in St Ives was a critical influence on her work. Historical precedents for the display of sculpture outdoors include the Battersea Park exhibition in London started in 1948, which was so successful that it continued and was also organised in Glasgow and Sheffield. The Grizedale Forest programme was influenced by increased environmental awareness and inspired by the Land Art movement developed in the 1960s by artists such as Robert Smithson and Nancy Holt who made artworks directly in the landscape, often in North America, as well as wider shifts in the creative use of site by British artists such as Richard Long who pioneered the making of art by walking in the landscape. It also formed part of a wider movement of artists working in different contexts pioneered by the Artist Placement Group, founded in 1966 by John and Barbara Latham, and other residency opportunities founded around that time such as those at Durham Cathedral and Portland Quarry.

Fusing many of these precedents, the Grizedale Forest artist-in-residence programme established the forest as a working environment for sculptors alongside foresters and farmers. Rather than a sculpture park presenting works outdoors, the residencies led to the creation of a new and unique body of sited work across the forest. Grizedale Forest provided sculptors with the opportunity to create work directly on site, using the forest as a studio, rather than simply exhibiting their work in a gallery outdoors as in a more traditional sculpture park.

Works were often developed in response to specific locations in which the work was created and installed. Growing on Silurian slate, the forest itself is full of sculptural qualities and potential; initially the majority of works were made from wood and stone. David Nash, the first artist to create a sculpture in Grizedale Forest, *Running Table* (1978), transported an entire tree trunk on the roof of his Morris Minor to move materials into position. It was understood by the sculptors that works made of natural materials sourced from the forest would weather over time.

Nash captured this ethos in *Sense of Place* (1984), the first of many publications about art in the landscape at Grizedale:

i. The sculptures should work with the environment using the materials and conditions the Forest naturally has to offer.

ii. The sculptors should acknowledge the relationship of the forest and those who work it; using their materials and tools and calling on their experience of planting, growing, tending [and] cutting.

iii. The placing of sculptures should activate otherwise neutral spaces and not occupy areas that already have a positive sense of 'place'.

Foresters were deeply involved with the artists during their time in the forest, providing accommodation and all manner of support in the extremely remote rural setting. Artists' residencies typically lasted around six months and often involved enduring exceedingly wet weather as well as the remote conditions. The first artist-in-residence to be appointed, Richard Harris, returned several times, creating multiple works over many years, and this was true of several of the artists. Harris was the first to make a work that drew inspiration from the intricate network of Cumbrian dry-stone walls laced across the forest and the wider surrounding landscape: *Dry Stone Passage* (1982) (see photo on p. 86) immerses the viewer in a dry-stone wall corridor which turns the walker through the landscape, framing the wooded outlook and at certain times the position of the sun.

Richard Harris met his wife, sculptor Sally Matthews, at Grizedale. Her figurative works, such as *Cry in the Wilderness* (1993), depicting a pack of wolves gathered on a rocky outcrop, and *Wild Boar* (1989), in which a small group of animals are set among the trees, were made from mud, cement and brash on metal armatures. Both the sensitivity of her sculpting and their inspired placement caused many a walker to do a double-take when encountering them and made them much-loved works.

Grizedale Forest launched the careers of many now internationally renowned artists by providing a platform for the creation of both temporary, experimental and ephemeral works and ambitious landscape-scale works which had not before been available to younger, emerging practitioners. One of the most notable of these artists is Andy Goldsworthy whose major works at Grizedale included *Seven Spires* (1984), the largest installation in the forest at that time. As the name suggests, this was a series of seven vertical spires made from straight timber trunks, cathedral-like, reaching high up into the canopy. In the following year, he created the immense *Sidewinder* which was made of bent and curved tree trunks which were not of commercial value to sawmills, creating an enormous horizontal wooden wiggle-shaped form weaving through the trees. Visually and formally, *Sidewinder* connected to the iconic *Taking a Wall for a Walk* (1990) which was made from the vernacular dry-stone walling technique of the surrounding Cumbrian Fells. The wall wove its way down a steep forest hillside, meandering between a straight line of plantation trees. It became one of Goldsworthy's and Grizedale Forest's most famous works. The collection of works resulting from the residencies quickly accumulated and at its peak, in the mid-1990s, there were around 90 sited works distributed across the network of waymarked trails.

# Evolution of the Forest as Recreational Experience

In 1965 Martin Orram won a Western European Scholarship to study land management innovations in Holland, where they were creating forests specifically for people to visit rather than for productive forestry, having drained a polder and planted it with trees and installed nature trails. On his return, Orram was appointed Specialist Recreation Developer and, following the Countryside Acts of 1967 (Scotland) and 1968 (England and Wales) which provided the right for the Forestry Commission to engage in public recreation, he became Head of Design at the Commission's Head Office in Edinburgh, leading on interpretation for the UK. Foresters were encouraged to attend new training courses about opening up forests to the public.

A governmental committee, which included the Countryside Commission, Nature Conservancy and the Forestry Commission, identified that at this time there were around 500 nature trails in Britain and Dartington Amenity Research Trust in Devon was engaged to evaluate them. It discovered that most trails provided a leaflet but that after the first stop visitors put the leaflet in their pockets. What they really liked was waymarked trails which helped them to avoid getting lost and made it easier to follow the trails. Written text and leaflets were clearly not the most effective way to engage people if they were not being read. Artists, as lateral thinkers, were called on to expand the remit of the foresters in connecting with the public.

### The Beginner's Way: Haldon Forest

As a result of this Jamie McCullough created The Beginner's Way, a pioneering interactive trail in Haldon Forest in Devon. It was a physical and symbolic journey of approximately 2 kilometres, reflecting on the process of creation. Jamie lived and worked on site, creating a series of 22 sequential environmental sculptures made from materials found in the forest. The trail was full of attractive details: a small curved bridge off the ground which would settle as you walked onto it, stepping stones across the water providing challenge and excitement, and a stone in a cave under which people left a little food for the next visitor.

The installations were open to the public and created a playful journey through the forest which heightened the senses by drawing attention to the environment. McCullough would not permit any form of marketing or promotion: he was adamant that visitors experiencing it for the first time should come upon it by chance and then return with friends. Its reputation did indeed build by word of mouth; numerous offers from TV and magazines that had discovered the popularity and originality of the work were declined. On the busiest days more than 1,000 people were drawn to the magical wooded walk and in the few short years that the work existed it attracted an estimated half-a-million visits. Traces of the installation still exist and continue to be visited by those who return with fond memories of it.

## Sculpture Trail: The Forest of Dean

In 1986 the Forest of Dean Sculpture Trail was established. The pioneering Martin Orram moved to the area and transplanted the knowledge acquired at Grizedale Forest, developing a new model for commissioning sculptures, this time on a bespoke new trail. This was made possible with the dedicated partnership and curatorial support of Jeremy Rees, Founding Director and Rupert Martin, Curator from the Arnolfini gallery in Bristol. Several of the early artists-in-residence at Grizedale, including David Nash and Keir Smith, were among the artists commissioned for the Sculpture Trail along with other key figures from British sculpture, such as Ian Hamilton Finlay and Peter Randall-Page, and international practitioners.

The sculptures' locations were chosen by the artists who were invited to select sites within a 30-minute walk of the main arrival point in the forest. After the sculptures were installed a trail was devised to link them, which initially took about an hour and a half to walk. This was in contrast to the model developed at Grizedale Forest where works were created across the entire forest, offering a wide area for visitors to explore and take in all of the pieces. Keir Smith's *Iron Road* (1986) used the route of an existing disused railway embankment running through the forest, formerly used for mining, which intersects with the trail. *Iron Road* is formed from a series of 20 jarrah railway sleepers, each carved with an individual image of a natural or industrial motif – a feather, a leaf, a wheel, a factory or a cloud. The images appear again and again, their sequence along the road implying an unknown narrative drawn from the forest's industrial and natural heritage. This original work is still *in situ* today.

The ethos of embracing the decay of natural materials at Grizedale was addressed differently in the Forest of Dean. Many of the original commissions still exist, including *Hanging Fire* (1988), an early work by Cornelia Parker, and *Cathedral* (1986) by Kevin Atherton, having been carefully protected to withstand the elements and forming a sensitively conserved core collection. Where several decades' decay of natural materials has inevitably necessitated decommissioning, a creative approach has been pioneered, using it as an opportunity to celebrate the works and create something new from them.

Magdelena Jetelova's iconic sculpture *Place* (1986), made from gigantic timbers and known locally as The Giant's Chair, architectonically recalled prehistoric structures such as Stonehenge. It was greatly loved, being visible across a large stretch of the forest when it was first installed at the start of the trail since the trees were young and did not obscure the view from far away. In 2015 *Place* was conceptually completed, in line with Jetelova's original intentions, by being charcoaled *in situ*. Artist Onya McClausand then created *Charcoal Measure* (2016), using the charcoal to draw bold lines across the forest floor by scoring trenches marking the coal seams 305 metres below.

Close partnership between the Forestry Commission and the Forest of Dean Sculpture Trust has maintained a consistent focus on the practice of sculpture and on working in direct response to the specific site. Thoughtfully curated new site-specific commissions have been added to the trail, often continuing exploration of the unique geology and mining heritage of the Dean as well as the dynamics of the working forest and its history. Examples include sculptures such as *Raw* (2001) by Neville Gabie, a wooden cube constructed from every piece of timber milled from a single felled oak planted in 1810, and *Echo* (2008) by Annie Cattrell, a detailed resin cast of a quarry that is sited in the same quarry and glistens from being infused with metallic powder.

There have been commissions in other art forms too, most notably *Lightshift* (2001) which presented 25 works by a team of artists led by Mark Anderson and Robin Blackledge. It was a major night-time light event to mark reopening of the forest after closure due to foot-and-mouth. Hugely successful at attracting visitors back, it was attended by 40,000 people over seven nights, all eager to reconnect with the forest and witness the extraordinary spectacle of light, fire, projection and sound installations at night.

## The Art & Architecture Programme: Kielder Forest

Kielder Forest has changed considerably over the last decades. From being the largest conifer-timber-producing forest in England with little recreation and tourism, it has been transformed into an award-winning cultural destination. Planning for recreation at Kielder started to come into focus in the mid-1970s with the creation of Kielder Dam leading to Kielder Water. Following this, a number of partner organisations started to move into the area with Northumbrian Water, Calvert Trust and Scout Association all creating venues for visitor experiences around the waterside.

The Kielder Art & Architecture programme started in 1995 as a photography residency and also with sculpture commissions. The sheer scale of Kielder Forest, the largest man-made forest in England, and Kielder Water, a reservoir which is the largest man-made lake in Europe, requires works of art that are destinations. The artworks here punctuate a vast landscape of 62,000 hectares, attracting visitors to travel long distances across the forest by car, bike or hiking to discover them. *Viewpoints* (1998), a two-part sculpture by Tania Kovats, sited on the opposite shores of the lake, is a scaled rendering of the viewpoints symbol found on Ordnance Survey maps and presented at the equivalent life-sized scale. Kovats says that 'Viewpoints are heroic, strategic or quiet. They are destinations.'

The unique characteristic of being an art and architecture programme provides distinctiveness to the forest commissions and the works on an architectural scale address the landscape with the confidence and purpose it demands. They include *Minotaur* (2003), a maze by Nick Coombe and Shona Kitchen, located adjacent to Kielder Castle; James Turrell's circular and most impressive *Skyspace* (2000), sited atop Cat Cairn with views across the 11-kilometre length of Kielder Water; and Chris Drury's *Wave Chamber* (1996), a beehive-shaped camera obscura 4 metres high, made from 80 tonnes of stone sited on the shores of the lake. These are all structures and enclosures which at once offer varying degrees of shelter and reframe the vast surroundings, literally reflecting and refracting the sky, light and water of their environment.

Kielder's Art & Architecture programme developed the Dark Sky Observatory by Charles Barclay Architects in 2008. The success of this as an attraction has helped to develop off-peak tourism in the area and led to recognition of Kielder Water & Forest Park as the first International Dark Sky Park in the country in 2013 – it is in fact the third-largest protected Dark Sky reserve in the world. In the same year Kielder Water & Forest Park was awarded Best Tourism Experience National Award from Visit England. Today Kielder Observatory hosts towards 40,000 visits per year, including late evening events starting at 11pm. This has helped evolve a year-round tourism offer in Northumberland and in turn ensured year-round tourism-related employment.

## The Enchanted Forest: Faskally Wood

Dark skies and the forest at night have also been a source of inspiration north of the border. The Enchanted Forest event was created by James McDougal of Forestry Commission Scotland (now Scottish Forestry); it is now held at Forestry and Land Scotland's Faskally Wood in Highland Perthshire and is Scotland's premier sound and light event. The event was launched in 2002 at The Hermitage, a National Trust for Scotland site near Dunkeld, and was developed as an innovative way to promote forest recreation and to show the autumn woodlands in a new light and offer an innovative experience for tourists in what is traditionally the start of the off-peak season. It is now an annual event during which a team of lighting and sound designers transform the natural surroundings of Faskally Wood into a stunning outdoor experience. Drawing on a wide range of inspiration, the creative team design a journey through the woodland, contrasting visual spectacles with moments of calm. The lighting is set to an original music score which combines contemporary and traditional creating a rousing experience to stir the senses. Originally a five-day event attracting 1,800 visitors, the Enchanted Forest has grown to become one of the largest outdoor events in Scotland, attracting 80,000 visitors over four weeks and five weekends in 2018.

The event has also had a huge impact on the local community. The Enchanted Forest Community Trust has overseen the running and implementation of the event to the benefit of the local area since 2010 and a recent report revealed that the event boosts the local economy by £7.66 million each year. It has also received numerous awards, including

Best Cultural Event at the UK Event Awards 2016 and Best Outdoor Festival at the Scottish Outdoor and Leisure Awards 2017.

## Stour Valley Arts: King's Wood, Kent

Stour Valley Arts was launched in 1993 in King's Wood, a 400-hectare ancient woodland in Kent, by a committee formed of the Kentish Stour Countryside Project, South East Arts, Forestry Commission, Ashford Borough Council and Kent County Council. This programme commissioned pieces by some artists who had made works in other forests, including Richard Harris and Chris Drury, and also worked in new forms of land art using tree planting and sound. Jem Finer's *Score for a Hole in the Ground* (2006) uses a sculptural horn above ground combined with falling water on percussive instruments in the ground, to create music inspired by Japanese water chimes. Rosie Leventon's *B52* (2004) is an area of sweet chestnut cleared to create the shape of a B52 bomber with a wingspan of 112 metres. Made from a void in the growing trees of the forest, it offers a different perspective for both viewers on the ground and planes or birds flying above the canopy.

Residencies here were based in a converted former forester's office on site. Artists, such as renowned walking artist Hamish Fulton, were often invited to make performative or temporary works in the landscape and these were often accompanied by high-quality publications. London Fieldworks created *Super Kingdom* (2009), an ambitious installation of show homes for animals. These clusters of birdbox-like structures, which swarmed on a number of large specimen trees, were inspired by Mussolini's Palazzo della Civiltà Italiana, Stalin's unbuilt Moscow Palace of the Soviets, and Ceaușescu's The People's House in Bucharest, now the Palace of the Parliament. Stour Valley Arts also created an extensive and ambitious forest-based educational programme, working with schools, families and the local community, connecting people with nature through creativity and with creativity through nature.

## Fermynwoods Contemporary Art: Fermyn Woods and Fineshade Wood

Founded in 1998, Fermynwoods Contemporary Art is an educational charity that commissions innovative and meaningful ways for visual artists to engage with audiences and enables a wide range of temporary, engagement and education projects in public spaces across Northamptonshire and online. They use Fermyn Woods and Fineshade Wood in Northamptonshire as a base for activities enabling artists, participants and audiences to explore the woods in new ways. Edwina fitzPatrick's 'The Archive of the Trees' (2018) residency and exhibition explored the relationship between trees and climate change by taking sampled cores from a range of species in Fineshade Wood. The exhibition in the newly refurbished Arches gallery space featured two-sided vertical prints, which revealed both the bark and interiors of the cored trees. The leaves blowing into the Arches during autumn added to the effect of the exhibition being in a forest.

## The Big Art Project: Sutton Manor

Not all arts projects in forests have been rurally based. In 2006 Sutton Manor in St Helens, Merseyside became the focus of the most ambitious project to date in our public forests. The newly planted community woodland on the regenerated site of a former colliery was one of a handful selected from a UK-wide search to feature on *The Big Art Project*, a major national public art initiative launched by Channel 4. Liverpool Biennial led the commissioning process with close involvement of the former miners of the colliery, supporting development of the vision for the programme and selection of the artist. Spanish artist Jaume Plensa was chosen to create a new work for the site in 2007. His sculpture *Dream*, 20 metres high, presents the elongated head of a nine-year-old girl. Her closed eyes suggest she is dreaming of both her own future and that of the former colliery site and the local community. *Dream* became the focal successful project of the Channel 4 series which aired in 2009 and Melvyn Bragg described as 'a cultural monument for a class'.

# Building for the Future

Over the decades the Forestry Commission has learned how best to manage the complex challenges involved in commissioning, co-commissioning, curating, installing, interpreting, maintaining, archiving, conserving and decommissioning contemporary art in forest environments. Much expertise has been developed from an understanding of when it has worked well and when it could have worked better. As well as the original and diverse opportunities it provides, particular challenges have been presented by the forest environment. The necessity to decommission decaying but much-loved works involves a delicate balance between the artists' original intentions, health and safety requirements, and visitors' desire to return to beloved favourites and discover them in favourable condition. Also the particular demands of forest management – the felling and replanting of trees, and the impact of the weather and windblown trees changing the context of the artworks – have created unusual maintenance and conservation considerations.

The Forestry Commission has learnt that art in forests works best when the subject and focus of the work are rooted in the forest itself. From its beginnings in Grizedale, the Commission has developed and sustained a unique formula of offering patronage to artists, providing opportunities to create work rooted in the forest context, and, through that, building engagement with visitors to the forest. The intrinsic value of the inspiration forests provide and the value of interpreting them through art remains central. The Commission has developed a mature model for the 21st century and works in partnership with Arts Council England, delivering a continuing collaboration with other arts organisations to create opportunities to reinterpret forests in new art forms. There is a mix of site-specific programmes and temporary and touring projects that can be presented at a number of sites.

*Living Symphonies*

In 2014 *Living Symphonies* was composed and realised by James Bulley and Daniel Jones. It was co-commissioned and co-produced by Forestry Commission England in partnership with Sound And Music, and toured to Thetford Forest in Norfolk, Fineshade Woods in Northamptonshire, Cannock Chase Forest in Staffordshire and Bedgebury Pinetum in Kent, evolving as it toured. A musical composition that grows in the same way as a forest ecosystem, it portrayed the thriving activity of the forest's wildlife, plants and atmospheric conditions, creating an ever-changing symphony heard among the forest itself. The music evolved live and adapted to the weather conditions of the site in real time. The symphony was critically acclaimed and was innovative in both its form and fusing of site-specific ecology and the latest digital technology.

A Wales of Vibrant Culture

Two years after Forestry Commission Wales split from its sister agencies in England and Scotland to become part of Natural Resources Wales in 2013, the Well-being of Future Generations (Wales) Act gave a duty to all public bodies in Wales to work together to deliver seven well-being goals, one of which was for 'A Wales of vibrant culture and thriving Welsh language'. Contemporary art and performance in outdoor settings are very much a part of the cultural tradition in Wales. Its landscape has been the incubator for iconic work such as David Nash's *Ash Dome*, grown from a sapling in a remote valley in Snowdonia but recognised around the world. The Welsh public forest has also been the muse and canvas for works of international significance. In 2015 Helen Sear took her subtle yet powerful piece …*The Rest Is Smoke* from the regimented rows of Monmouthshire forestry to the winding waterways of Venice, becoming the first woman to represent Wales at the Venice Biennale.

The spirit of collaboration between the cultural and environmental sectors continues in Wales's public woodlands. The summer of 2019 saw the artists' residency 'Egin' (the Welsh word for 'bud' or 'shoot') being held in Snowdonia in partnership with National Theatre Wales, the British Council, Snowdonia National Park Authority and the National

Trust. It invited artists to have a creative conversation with climate change and sustainable development specialists and to create a space where new work could germinate.

## Jerwood Open Forest

In 2013 Forestry Commission England launched a new initiative called Jerwood Open Forest, inviting artists to take the lead in determining the location and art form in which to propose new artworks for forests in England. Through a partnership with Jerwood Charitable Foundation, artists were invited to propose bold and ambitious ideas in any art form, for any duration, located anywhere in a public forest. Five diverse projects were selected for a six-month research and development period. Supported by Arts Council England, it was an innovative model for commissioning, supporting emerging artists with a bursary to give them space and time to test new ideas in response to public forests. Through two editions of the initiative, three projects have been fully realised through awards of £30,000 each: *Hrafn: Conversations with Odin* composed by Chris Watson and produced by Iain Pate in 2014; *Cosmos* by Semiconductor, also in 2014; and *Joyride* by Keith Harrison in 2017.

*Hrafn: Conversations with Odin* was a multi-channel, spatialised sound installation featuring the remarkable, and seldom-witnessed, conversations of thousands of ravens returning to roost. The sound installation took place in Kielder Water & Forest Park on three consecutive nights in October 2014. Audiences were led at twilight into the deepest part of the forest. Settling down as darkness fell, participants heard the sounds of 2,000 birds arriving in the canopy overhead to begin their conversations. Watson's composition started with the calls of distant ravens and concludes with a full raven roost overhead. The work anticipated and celebrated the return of these powerful voices to the forest, making a connection back to Norse mythology. This completely ephemeral artwork lives on the memory of those who experienced it and itself has become part of the folklore of the forest.

## Festival in the Forest

Grizedale Forest remains a test bed for innovation and hosted the first ever Abandon Normal Devices digital arts and film festival in 2010, which returned to the forest again in 2015. *In the Eyes of the Animal*, a virtual reality artwork by the creative studio Marshmallow Laser Feast, was co-commissioned in partnership with Abandon Normal Devices. It was created in Grizedale using the latest Lidar scanning, drones and bespoke 360-degree cameras, and included audio recordings sourced from the forest. Viewers were able to experience Grizedale through the eyes of four different species native to the forest: midge, dragonfly, frog and owl. Premiering at the Festival in the Forest, it has since toured the globe including to the prestigious Sundance Film Festival, achieving popular and critical acclaim and multiple nominations and awards in recognition for its originality in the emerging art form of virtual reality. It can now also be experienced online through use of Google cardboard.

## A Sculpture for the Centenary

Fittingly, the Forestry Commission's centenary has been marked by the creation of a new permanent sculpture by Rachel Whiteread, one of this country's most important living artists and the first woman to win the Turner Prize. A co-commission with 14–18 NOW, the First World War Centenary programme, *Nissen Hut* (2018) is part of Whiteread's international Shy Sculpture Series. Found deep in Yorkshire's Dalby Forest, one of the first sites to be acquired by the Commission in 1919, the sculpture is a ghostly white cabin made by casting in concrete the interior space of a nearby Nissen hut, a prefab military structure invented during the First World War and used to house the workers involved in the planting of the forest. Whiteread has said of the sculpture: 'the work becomes a sort of testament to its own history and weathers into the place'. This new monument brings visitors into the heart of the forest, a living, breathing space in which to view art.

# CHAPTER 6
# Cities

## An Urban Forest?

It may seem strange to talk about 'cities' and 'forestry' in the same sentence. We think of forests as being exclusively rural, and until about 40 years ago the two were seen as quite distinct. Today, however, in our increasingly urbanised society, there are a number of areas of overlap. The involvement of city dwellers volunteering in Community Forests (regeneration projects in England based on creating new forests and wooded areas) and the creation of peri-urban forests (forests and woodlands surrounding towns and cities which might be included in both rural and urban administrations) have blurred the lines between urban and rural. Networks of green spaces and city treescapes, areas along linear routes such as waterways and amenity areas, have increasingly been regarded as contributing to an urban ecosystem: an urban forest.

In the early days of the Forestry Commission, timber production (much of which took place in the uplands) was the main drive for tree planting and the focus was on production forestry and the rural economy. Today, it is widely accepted that trees and woods have many purposes which are not mutually exclusive. Just as in the countryside, so in our cities well-managed woodlands can provide recreation, combat flooding, and store carbon as well as producing timber. Trees and woods in and around our cities provide shade and temperature moderation, help intercept or mitigate air pollution, attract and support wildlife, play an important screening and beautifying role, and can provide useful products.

Forestry in towns and cities is now a deliberate policy in many countries and a significant component of urban greening. In Britain, a current working definition of urban forestry is 'the care and management of individual trees and tree populations to improve the environment in and around urban areas', suggesting that all trees – private and public, in woods or on streets, small and large, young and old, common or exotic – are a part of the urban forest. Unlike its rural counterpart, however, the urban forest is rarely under the ownership or management of one person or organisation, and trees in an urban setting are often subject, like their human counterparts, to an urban lifestyle. They set their seed and drop their leaves on an impermeable surface; they are exposed to the abuses of pollution, but also to the benefits of human cultivation.

The term 'urban forestry' was coined by Erik Jorgensen, professor at the University of Toronto, who introduced it to a British audience in a paper at the 10th Commonwealth Forestry Conference in 1974 – ironically as a response to Dutch elm disease. Today we use the term 'urban forest' to describe something that is in part planned and in part natural. Although people in the past may not have used that term and may not have had designed spaces with trees and open land, they would have recognised the relationship between people and the trees close to where they lived. The connection with trees such as the Ankerwycke Yew opposite Runnymede and the Tolpuddle Martyrs' tree in Dorset clearly predates the concept of today's urban forest, and many ancient trees demonstrate a close human connection with trees for spiritual and cultural reasons. For millennia, settlements have included and used trees for construction, tools, fuel, fodder and a host of other products essential to daily life.

Trees have been deliberately used in towns and cities from at least the 16th century. Later, a mix of private gardens and walks became available to the wider population (at a charge), while avenues and treed squares in affluent areas became part of the urban landscape. During the early 20th century municipal government became responsible for street trees and parks, employing professional arboriculturalists to both plant and care for large numbers of trees. Two world wars put brakes on growth of the urban treescape but the desire to make trees part of the urban landscape had become established. As early as 1932 the Town and Country Planning Act enabled planning authorities to protect amenity – including trees. In 1947 Tree Preservation Orders 'to protect public amenity' indicated a shift away from protecting trees as personal property but rather as a public good. Nevertheless, well-treed areas of towns and cities remained the preserve of the more wealthy, and 'green and leafy suburbs' described a setting that was not available to many.

The reclamation of damaged areas after the Second World War, which was linked to growing affluence, rekindled resources and an interest in urban trees. Some towns and cities recognised the value of their urban woods. The focus, though, remained clearly on the collections of individual trees; forestry and arboriculture remained artificially distinct.

# The Forestry Commission and Urban Forestry: First Steps

Given that 'forestry' is common parlance in today's urban agendas, it seems inevitable that the Forestry Commission would have been deeply involved in the thinking and advocacy for the role of trees in towns and cities. This began with its work in land reclamation in the late 1950s and gathered pace in the 1980s alongside a shifting attitude to urban forestry.

The Commission had been heavily involved in woodland establishment on restored opencast coal sites in Wales since 1958 and this experience was to prove immensely useful in the restoration of other brownfield sites, such as in the Rhondda. Forest Research built a considerable level of expertise and knowledge in this specialised area. From 1962 the Forestry Commission was also heavily involved in the planting of motorway and road schemes for the Department of Transport; by 1990 it had planted over 30 million trees in motorway verges. The Commission was also expert in establishing productive woodland in marginal habitats, through elevation, exposure, ground conditions or contamination. It was a natural partner in these new landscapes.

English oak *(Quercus robur)*

In 1963 Arthur C. Hazzard wrote in *The Journal of the Forestry Commission* about work the Commission had supported in the Rhondda:

Nowhere in all Britain does reafforestation offer such a challenge and, at the same time, such a reward, as in Wales's newest state forest – that of Rhondda. Here is a forest in the making actually within the boundaries of a borough; instead of the traditional forest 'village' it has a teeming population of a hundred thousand in its very centre.

Timber extraction over these steep slopes calls for no little skill in road engineering; the choice of species for Rhondda's exacting climate and its bewildering variety of aspect and soil conditions is itself a silvicultural challenge. Its rewards are no less exciting. With its vivid industrial history leading to the almost complete denudation of its former wealth of timber, Rhondda now faces a new look in which not only are the industrial blemishes largely covered but these scarred acres made to yield a crop of timber such as Rhondda has not seen extracted for 200 years. Already 20 families, scattered between Clydach Vale, Gelli, Y strad, Blaenrhondda, Treherbert, Cwm parc and Treorchy find their livelihood from the few hundred acres at Mynydd Tylacoch, Mynydd Maindy and Llwynypia Mountain now planted – that previously supported, if that is the right word in Rhondda, a few score of sheep.

In the 1970s new ideas about how we consider trees, woods and forests in and around cities began to spread from North America to Europe. In 1972 an Arboriculture Research Working Party was set up, including representatives from the Forestry Commission, which led to the appointment of an arboriculturist to focus on amenity trees, funded by the Department of the Environment, and three years later the Arboriculture Advisory and Information Service was established at the Forestry Commission's research station at Alice Holt. Proposals and projects were launched to raise the importance of trees in the public mind, along with attempts to raise the necessary resources in the public sector. The impact of Dutch elm disease galvanised politicians, organisations and the public to undertake a large-scale tree planting campaign.

In 1977 the Irish-born professor of forestry Laurence Roche clearly set out the case for bringing woods to the people at the British Association for the Advancement of Science, suggesting two responses to the demands of urban communities for access to woods and forests. One was to carefully open up and provide facilities in relatively small areas of established forest – something that the Forestry Commission was by then beginning to do as it started to open up the forests for public access and recreation. The other was to 'bring forests and woodland to the people; to intrude into the decaying centres of our great cities through the urban–rural interface'. Could local authorities not take this further and, with the assistance of the central authority, establish and manage Community Forests? It was to be some years before this idea came to fruition.

Dutch elm disease in Britain, one of the most notorious tree diseases (discussed in more detail on p. 145), has killed over 60 million British elms in two epidemics since the 1920s, transforming rural and urban landscapes and our relationship with trees. The Forestry Commission donated 70,000 trees to the Plant a Tree in '73 campaign and later gave a grant towards small-scale woodland creation in Havering in east London.

In Brighton and Hove a dedicated local campaign, council-led management plan and the area's natural geographical defences managed to keep the disease at bay. Strict monitoring and inspections of the elm stock allowed diseased trees to have infection removed by pruning affected branches or felling the tree to remove its beetle breeding potential. Brighton and Hove has gained international acclaim for this work and in 1998 was given the guardianship of the National Collection of Ulmus (Elms) by the National Council for the Conservation of Plants and Gardens. The area now has the largest remaining population of mature elm trees in the UK and the greatest diversity of elm types of any city in the world. Elms are a point of local pride for locals and are hugely valued by the city.

The Forestry Commission's involvement in urban forestry in the 1980s was driven initially by opportunity and pragmatism. The Commission's Annual Report of 1980–81 stated that 'priority [is] being given to revenue earning developments, such as forest cabins, campsites and sporting, and to visitor centres and popular day-visitor facilities, particularly those close to towns' – also an early recognition that closeness to people was an important part of its offer.

From 1980 the Forestry Commission and the Arboricultural

Association held five-yearly seminars to update the arboriculture industry on current relevant research in the UK. A new arboricultural research contract amounting to £450,000 over three years was negotiated with the Department of the Environment to begin in January 1987. Studies of plant quality, urban trees and hedgerow trees were included and spread more widely; for example, Cutler and Richardson's book on *Tree Roots and Buildings* (1981) was supported by the Forestry Commission.

Britain's industrial capacity decreased by fully one-quarter during the years 1980–84. As 'dirty' industries declined, large areas of land were released that became known as 'brownfield'. Factories, steelworks and coalmines fell silent and rusting infrastructure became a part of the urban landscape.

Recession, urban decay, unemployment and wider social problems led to governments investing in property-led regeneration programmes with budgets to match. The large areas of brownfield, including mining and landfill areas, needed to be transformed to make new investment attractive and also to breathe new life into communities. The Forestry Commission got involved with these new programmes, drawing on its knowledge of land reclamation and its solid base of practical expertise backed by scientific research. The Commission's in-house magazine, *The Slasher*, reported in 1988 that the Commission had donated 30,000 trees, ranging from native oak and beech to more exotic snakebark maple and rare red elder, for planting in various urban areas throughout Britain, and that they were carried free by British Rail to Cardiff, Edinburgh, Manchester and Northampton. About 5,000 were made available to members of the public to 'take home and care for until ready for final planting in an appropriate site'.

The Commission began to work in new areas and with new partners different from those in traditional upland forestry. Programmes led by the then Department of Environment in the West Midlands involved local authorities – organisations relatively unfamiliar to the Forestry Commission at that time. Other bodies and organisations from landscape, wildlife and community perspectives were also keenly involved. Partnership working was the essence of delivery in this complex organisational and funding environmant. A number of embryonic urban forestry projects emerged in the 1980s, including Tower Hamlets. The Forest of London, Hyndburn and Motherwell projects were important catalysts led by innovative individuals from planning, arboriculture and environment backgrounds: town and country planners, landscape architects, arboriculturists employed by local authorities and consultants.

The National Garden Festivals, a government initiative promoted in 1980 by Michael Heseltine as environment secretary, aimed at creating new, attractive infrastructure in industrial derelict areas for a festival period that could then become the basis of regeneration and reclamation in years to follow. Five festivals were held, one every two years, starting with Liverpool in 1984. The Forestry Commission was involved, largely as a means to promote rural forestry to a wider public audience. In Scotland the Central Scotland Countryside Trust (CSCT) was set up in 1985, following work by Lothian Council to improve degraded land through the Central Scotland Woodland Project. The Trust was made up of seven local authorities and the Countryside Commission for Scotland – another indication that partnership was becoming the default way of working in delivery projects.

# Urban Forestry for Local Communities

A notable shift in thinking within the Forestry Commission developed from the early days of planting for land reclamation towards more urban and urban-fringe projects. Initially, forestry planting was dominated by commercial conifer species such as larch and spruce with small areas of broadleaves to integrate with the landscape and provide varied habitats for wildlife. Forestry in urban areas involved sites that were generally smaller and fragmented so less appropriate for commercial plantings. Also, community involvement indicated that people wanted more broadleaved trees. Commercial considerations were a lower priority compared with openness, the changing seasons and wildlife. Urban forests included some commercial elements but broadleaved amenity woodland dominated.

At local level the Forestry Commission assisted in the development of many of these projects. In 1986 a Black Country working party had been set up and a Commission secondee was joint-funded as Urban Forester

– perhaps the first employee with this title in the organisation. In the West Midlands the Forestry Commission was also heavily involved in the 'Seed in Time' conference of 1988. As the first conference in the UK to focus specifically on urban forestry, it raised the profile of urban forestry at a national level and marked the establishment of a national urban forestry movement, as well as acting as a further spur to action for the Black Country Urban Forestry Initiative. Two years later the Black Country Urban Forestry Unit was set up, supported by the advice of a part-time forester provided by the Forestry Commission.

The Commission's Annual Report of 1987-88 stated:

> We are very much involved in urban forestry, both directly because we manage something of the order of 90,000 hectares of woodlands close to towns, and indirectly through grant aid, research and training.

The Commission undertook to prepare a handbook of urban forestry, summarising research knowledge and practical experience, and cooperated closely with the Countryside Commission in this field.

Since 1970 the Countryside Commission had done work on the urban fringe in the north-west of England and east London, seeking to regenerate land affected by planning blight, fragmented and difficult agriculture, waste disposal following slum clearance, vandalism, trespass and neglect. Interventions were generally small scale and very localised. In order to have impacts at scale in the urban fringe, new woods and forests linked to changes in the planning system and countryside management services were discussed as possible solutions.

In 1986 the Countryside Commission published a draft policy statement entitled 'Forestry and the Countryside' which proposed 40,000 hectares of new multipurpose lowland forest as a resource for the nation, 'such a forest possibly located in the Midlands' which 'should be complemented by the establishment of other urban fringe forests where the main purpose would be the creation of attractive recreation sites close to centres of large urban populations'. The final policy statement in the following year firmed up its urban-fringe forestry aspirations, announcing a six-month feasibility study – with the involvement of the Forestry Commission – into a multipurpose lowland forest in the English Midlands. A joint statement was scheduled for mid-1988 on an initiative to create forests around major conurbations, to be followed by a prospectus.

After much discussion, in July 1989 the government gave the green light to the Community Forest programme. Starting in east London, the west Midlands and the North East, the family of 12 forests in Newcastle, Middlesbrough, Sheffield, Manchester, Liverpool, Nottingham, Birmingham, Bristol, Swindon, Bedford, and north and east London was complete by 1993.

The Forestry Commission provided technical assistance and advice, as well as access to research and grant funding. Its staff were seconded into forest teams to provide on-the-spot advice and support to landowners on woodland establishment, management and grants. The Countryside Commission provided half the core costs of the Community Forests' teams; the other half was met by local authority partners. The Forests had a wide-ranging and bold set of objectives, including regenerating the environment of the Green Belt and equivalent area, improving the landscape and environment near housing and industry, creating opportunities for sport and recreation, protecting areas of natural interest, and achieving a high level of community involvement. Timber production came fairly low down the list. All Community Forests aimed to substantially increase woodland cover to around 30 per cent of open land.

The objectives are an indication of the diversity of perceived benefits that woods and forests could bring at the time, though now they are supplemented by several others. A significant change was the inclusion and prominence given to forestry for people and communities. If the urban forest was to be relevant to its location and audience, it had to appeal to and provide benefits to local people who did not appreciate having solutions 'imposed' on their neighbourhoods. The tradition of forestry established in some rural areas was absent in the towns; instead urban dwellers valued views in their neighbourhood, wanted to walk and take leisure safely and in a welcoming environment, and wanted to be directly involved, be consulted and understand decisions. The new post of Community Forestry Officer was added to the Forestry Commission's team with a wide remit to advise and support the development of the small explosion of similar projects throughout Britain.

In 1991, over 5,000 square kilometres was selected to plant what was

CITIES

to become the National Forest in the Midlands. Spanning parts of Derbyshire, Leicester and Staffordshire, the landscape had a legacy of open-cast coal mining that blighted both the environment and local economy. A new forested area would transform land use and help deliver a new economic and social focus. Urban forestry had arrived on the main stage and although the National Forest was directly sponsored by central government, the Forestry Commission was again heavily involved in delivery, helping design and finance a tender scheme for woodland creation, and one of its Commissioners, Bridget Bloom, was appointed director of the National Forest Company.

In Scotland, the CSCT's objectives – on a 100-year timescale – were broadly similar to those in English forestry projects, including planting and management of woodlands, landscaping of main transport corridors, along with the creation of village nature parks and the creation and protection of wildlife habitats. They also aimed to work with the local business community to create both jobs and training in countryside skills and contribute to the wider debate on the Scottish environment. By the 1990s the proposals had attracted the attention of the Secretary of State for Scotland who proposed the formation of and financial support for the Central Scotland Woodlands Company.

In Wales the Commission did not directly follow the English model as it already had plans regarding the urban fringe. The Forest of Cardiff had been established with local authorities and the Countryside Commission, so existing Forestry Commission woodland was to be extended into the Valleys, with the Welsh Valleys Forest Initiative being launched in October 1992.

Forest Research continued to provide up-to-date technical information and guidance on using trees and woods in land reclamation. In 1993 it published *The Potential for Woodland Establishment on Landfill Sites* for the Department of the Environment, indicating both the rise of interest in forestry as a beneficial after-use of difficult land and the Commission's relevance across government departments. Wildlife, landscape design and public access were 'designed in', and staff training, seminars and site visits helped spread the word.

*Handbook 5: Urban Forestry Practice* (1989) set a marker for the Commission's intention to give new projects the best possible support and advice in urban and community forestry. A spate of publications followed, with a series of design guidelines focusing on community woodlands, lowland landscape, nature conservation, recreation and water. The Community Woodland Supplements specifically targeted grant aid at landowners in project areas.

Forest Enterprise was already a landowner in the programme areas and had been providing economic and recreation benefits for many years. The emerging Community Forest/National Forest programmes helped expand its landholding and develop a new customer focus to meet the new social agenda. Existing Forest Enterprise woods played a role as exemplars for what could be done in a new well-wooded and well-managed landscape. This provided impetus for new woodland creation in the programme areas aimed at mainly private landowners.

Through the late 1980s and early 1990s the programmes began to achieve real results, with woodland planting in some of the most difficult areas: old landfills and derelict 'brownfield' land, alongside socially deprived neighbourhoods where development 'hope value' was high. The impetus of Community Forests and the National Forest led to other areas in England setting up their own urban forestry projects, for example the White Rose Forest near Leeds and the Pennine Edge Forest near Manchester. In Scotland in the early 1990s, the Central Scotland Forest Trust (successor to the CSCT) became the primary organisation to continue the regeneration of degraded land between Edinburgh and Glasgow through community woodland creation. The Forestry Commission provided some core funding along with others and had a seat on the board.

# Urban Forestry for a New Millennium

The Forestry Commission's Land Regeneration Unit was set up in the 1990s with an express aim of developing expertise and giving practical operational guidance to enable the creation of public access community woodland on former industrial land where long-term liabilities might inhibit local authorities. In Nottinghamshire, Forest Enterprise and the County Council created a partnership that restored seven closed colliery spoil heaps to 760 hectares of new woodland and recreational space.

In 1998 England's Forestry Strategy included objectives to steadily increase forest cover, particularly around future urban and urban fringe development, where environmental improvements were key. Forest Enterprise could get involved as both landowner and manager of reclaimed sites and by creating new community woodlands.

European funds were targeted primarily within the agencies' areas and the environment began to be seen as a key driver for economic development. No longer was 'improve the look of the place' enough but attracting inward investment, jobs, improving quality of life for employees and their families became part of the expectation of funders. In addition, climate change and low carbon economics were increasingly accepted as part of the regeneration mix.

These trends brought greater challenge and opportunity for urban forests and the Forestry Commission. Investment needed to be justified in hard cost-benefit terms. Outputs and outcomes needed to show monetary values. The National Lottery, set up in 1993, was increasingly seen as a way to help finance projects. The Millennium Fund provided a focus for big projects and urban forestry organisations were not slow in putting together proposals: the Black Country Urban Forest was the winner of a grant, as was the Millennium Forest for Scotland, which included the Edinburgh Urban Forest Project (initiated in 1991).

The 1990s and 2000s were a time for growth, experimentation and expansion in urban and community forestry. Forestry in the urban realm was consolidating, delivering and showing visible evidence of growing new woods on previously bare land. Investment in trees, woods and forests was increasingly accepted as a substantial element of economic regeneration and in improving quality of life for some of the most economically and socially deprived areas of Britain. By 2000, the requirement for trees and woods, forming the urban forest as a major component of green infrastructure, was established as important in urban design, planning and meeting community needs. At the same time, devolution in Wales and Scotland, and regionalisation in England, began to shape more locally distinctive responses to economic and social development. Each country published its own Forestry Strategy and made strong references to forestry's relevance to economic, social, environmental and cultural dimensions and recognition that forestry spanned rural and urban locations. Urban forestry too was part of the change and was boosted by the publication in 2000 of the Urban White Paper 'Our Towns and Cities: The Future – Delivering an Urban Renaissance'. The establishment of Regional Development Agencies (RDAs) in England, as well as those agencies already in Wales and Scotland, created greater opportunities for urban forestry to deliver economic and social benefits.

Many public sector organisations, including the Forestry Commission, began to adopt an entrepreneurial approach in applying for funds to supplement falling budgets. In early 2000 the Forestry Commission won £9 million from the government's Capital Modernisation Fund to acquire and regenerate land in Merseyside, Thames Chase in Essex, and Red Rose Community Forests in Greater Manchester. The Land Regeneration Unit supported the work and over three years achieved 1,500 hectares of new woodland. In Essex within the M25, Page Wood was created on a 300-hectare site leased from Havering Borough Council, previously used as arable land and horse grazing. These new woodlands were of predominantly broadleaved trees – oak, ash, birch, black poplar, cherry, rowan and holly – although pine and larch were also included along with woody shrubs such as hazel, dogwood and guelder rose, to provide plant structure. Design was a new challenge with community consultation being critical to the success of the lines of paths, positions of seats, retaining views and promoting a sense of safety and welcome. Forest Enterprise produced a handbook on greenspace development projects in 2004 – an indicator of the growing focus on woods and green spaces for communities.

Launched in 2003 in the north-west of England, the Newlands project was a pioneer of targeted environmentally led regeneration instigated by the Forestry Commission. The Forest Services Area Team led the development of the project and especially the Public Benefit Recording System (PBRS) which systematically mapped and sifted over 3,000 sites for their potential to provide social, access, economic and environmental benefits. Forest Enterprise led on-site delivery alongside many other partners, including Community Forests, wildlife trusts and Groundwork. The North West Development Agency was persuaded by the PBRS and provided £32 million which, alongside other funding, led to eight large brownfield sites being transformed and adjacent streets

CITIES

planted with bespoke trees. The restoration of Moston Vale, a 24-hectare ex-landfill site in Manchester, involved capping the landfill with 50,000 tonnes of soil and the planting of thousands of trees including oak, larch, Douglas fir, birch, wild cherry and holly. The main objectives were to remediate the bownfield land to stimulate economic growth, improve social well-being, and create new habitats and widen biodiversity.

In Scotland the Forestry Commission had been largely supporting projects run by local authorities with cash, advice and presence on steering groups and boards, allied to the various woodland grants on offer. Devolution prompted a rethink on the role of forestry and urban areas. Previously the Commission had disposed of some woods in urban areas but the importance of ensuring forestry delivered for the urban public, close to home, led to the development of the Woodlands In and Around Towns (WIAT) programme. Forestry Commission Scotland visited some of the Community Forest areas, in particular those in north-west England, to see what might be transferrable. WIAT was a significant step forward and included a wide range of social, health, well-being and environmental priorities while continuing to provide economic benefits. It continues as a core initiative of Forestry Commission Scotland (now Scottish Forestry), having invested over £50 million since 2005 and will carry on to 2020 and beyond.

The Wales Woodland Strategy of 2001 recognised that forestry was predominantly rural-based but had an increasingly important role to play in urban regeneration, social and environmental justice, renewable energy and healthier lifestyles. It included the Cydcoed Initiative which ran in two phases: 2001–04 and 2003–08. Funded by the EU and the Welsh Assembly, Forestry Commission Wales (FCW) acted as the umbrella for the initiative, operating semi-independently. Cydcoed would help achieve the Welsh government's vision and FCW's Woodland for People element of its corporate plan, facilitating community forestry with all its benefits and involving local individuals in the decision-making. Work focused on communities with no access to green space and the most deprived communities in Wales. It was a new departure for FCW. The innovative delivery was not without humps and bumps but led to greater capacity in communities to be both more self-confident and self-reliant.

In 2002 the Forestry Commission established a London Conservancy in recognition of 'the value which trees, woodlands and green space have

213

in enhancing the social and environmental fabric of urban society'. The following year, a Regional Advisory Committee was established for London, again reinforcing the special role that trees and woods play in the capital. Alongside the policy work, Commission officers were busy advising on urban tree matters, including trees and subsidence on clay soils, utility companies and tree roots, insurance matters and tree safety. Many relationships were forged with partners in the capital, including tree officers, insurance companies, developers, architects and landscape architects as well as community groups and tree charities, for example the Trees and Design Action Group (TDAG). These partnerships aimed to continue to promote and establish trees and woods into the fabric of the city and more widely as the pressures on London's trees and woods were mirrored elsewhere. In 2005 a London Tree and Woodland Framework was launched as part of the Greater London Authority's (GLA) environment strategy. Forestry Commission and Forest Research teams helped set up a Right Trees for a Changing Climate website (www.righttrees4cc.org.uk) to advise public and professionals on the likely changes to the urban climate as well as existing harsh growing conditions in cities, when choosing trees. This resource is relevant to all urban areas.

Core funding from government to the Community Forest programme fund ran out in 2005. The government's intention was that momentum would be maintained through commitment and funding from local authorities, businesses and other local partners, assisted by new Regional Forestry Frameworks established by the Forestry Commission. In order to smooth the transition, the Commission was asked by government to provide two years of transitional support to the partnerships and to take the lead in the programme and in community forestry more generally. Nevertheless, it is fair to say that the loss of core funding had a long-term negative impact on the Community Forests. Although some have enjoyed good support from local authorities and successfully adjusted their business models and costs to adapt to more challenging circumstances, others have been left very exposed and a number of the organisations themselves have folded. More recently, a revival in citizen and government concern about urban trees, and vigorous efforts by the Community Forests themselves and their many passionate advocates, have begun to strengthen their position once more. Community Forests in the north of England, for example, are key partners along with the Woodland Trust in the important Northern Forest initiative, which seeks to mobilise public and private funding to support new woodland creation across a broad area of the north including a number of major conurbations.

Even at the time that funding for the Community Forests came to an end, however, central government continued to invest in other ways in forestry designed to directly benefit people in urban areas. In 2005, with funding from the government's Sustainable Communities Fund, the Commission acquired Jeskyns Farm in north Kent, part of the Thames Gateway growth area. The site was an intensive arable farm. Many of the natural habitats were degraded or lost and it was largely inaccessible to the public. The project aimed to transform it into multifunctional greenspace to benefit both the local environment and the thousands of current and future residents in the area. The community was involved from the outset and a programme of engagement was designed to determine their views on the design of the site. Through these consultations, it was decided to give the woodland an open feel, with meadows, shrub planting and orchards, in keeping with the traditional Kent countryside. The site opened in July 2007 and the number of visitors has increased year on year since then, with 330,000 visitors recorded in 2017–18 – a sevenfold increase on the original estimates. The woodland has also created many new habitats suitable for rare species. Community involvement has been hugely influential as the site has continued to evolve. A public consultation in 2012 led to the opening of a café and toilets at the site, which has contributed to increased visitor numbers and, importantly, made it more accessible to a wider range of visitors, especially those from previously underrepresented groups. In a remarkably short space of time, it has become a hugely successful green space for local people and wildlife alike and stands as an excellent example of the benefits that new woodlands can deliver in peri-urban areas.

From a broader policy perspective, it remained critical to the future of urban forestry to strengthen the recognition in the eyes of planning professionals and decision makers of the intimate relationship between trees and a healthy, attractive urban environment. In March 2009 Forest Research established the Urban Regeneration and Greenspace Partnership (URGP) which brought together a cross-government group and produced advice, guidance, research reports, evidence notes and publications to provide up-to-date support and information across a wide spectrum of organisations in urban planning, development and regeneration, while in 2010, the Forestry Commission published and promoted *The Case for Trees* to make the case for a fresh approach informed by this sort of evidence. In 2007 the government's Forestry Strategy in England reinforced the role of trees and woods in and around urban areas, building on and consolidating what had gone before. Greater emphasis was placed on communities, health, education and linking into green infrastructure more widely.

In 2010 the new Coalition Government announced the abolition of RDAs in England. Local authority budgets came under increasing pressure and urban and community forestry were now also subject to the same cost-benefit analysis as other departments. Increasingly the market benefits of trees, woods and green space were set out to justify the costs. Local authorities are now encouraged to produce Tree and Woodland Strategies, often developed in consultation with local communities, that take stock of all trees and woods and set out long-term proposals for their management and future scale and distribution.

In 2011 the government appointed an Independent Panel on Forestry to advise Defra on future direction. Its Report in 2012 emphasised the importance it placed on forestry in an urban environment:

We have a vision of a more wooded landscape and more woods closer to where people live. There is a place for urban trees, wooded parklands and hedgerows as much as for conifer plantations and small scattered woodlands within a broader landscape ...

We believe there should be more, and better maintained trees, close to where people live. This means more trees on urban streets, more trees in town parks, and tree 'corridors' from the centre of towns and cities out to local woods and forests with good access. We want people to enjoy the health benefits of access to trees and woodlands, and we want our urban areas to have more natural shade and to be more resilient to climate change.

The government responded by promising to 'focus particularly on woods close to our towns and cities where the greatest number of people can enjoy them'. The Forestry Commission in England took on an enabling role, recognising that it could achieve greater results by bringing people together rather than assuming the lead. In 2013 Regional Advisory Committees were renamed Forestry and Woodlands Advisory Committees (FWACs), with a remit to 'advise the Forestry Commission on implementing forestry' and 'support the government's interests by developing strong local connections and networks to enhance synergies across the forest and woodland sector'. The following year, the Commission established the Urban FWAC Network 'to take forward the case for urban forestry in England's towns and cities and spread good practice'. The Network set out its 'vision for a resilient urban forest' in 2016, declaring that it should 'be considered as critical infrastructure for urban areas, on a par with utility, transport and the built environment'.

In London, the Forestry Commission has been working with the GLA and the Mayor's Office to improve tree cover and tree health. It is an important member of the London Tree Partnership which was set up in 2011 as the RE:LEAF Partnership, with ambitious tree-planting and community-involvement programmes. The Commission ran a Tree and Woodland Community Grant for several years, and is a major player in the London Tree and Woodland Awards, which recognises the hard work put in by communities. A tree care guide aimed at those wishing to plant in cities was produced in partnership with Groundwork and the NHS Forest project which aims to provide green spaces with trees for people on or near NHS sites in the UK. Work continues in London and nationally with leading organisations in the urban tree field, including the TDAG, the London Tree Officers Association, the Arboriculture Association, National Association of Tree Officers and civil society groups such as the Tree Council, Trees for Cities and the Woodland Trust.

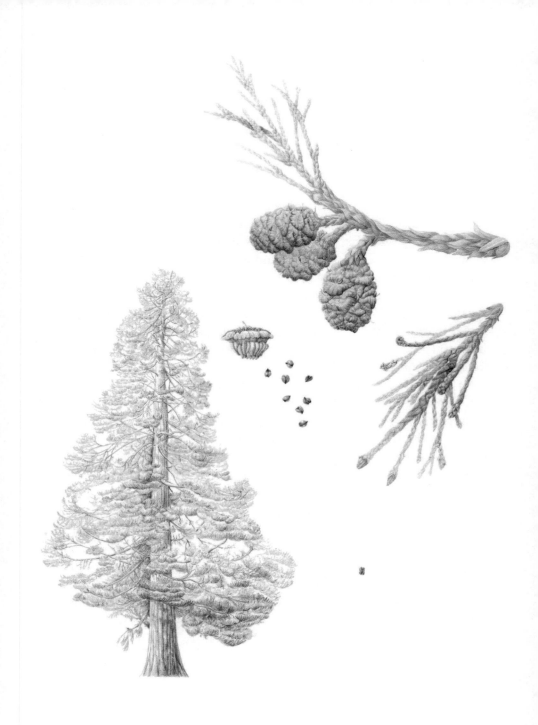

Giant sequoia *(Sequoiadendron giganteum)*

# Urban Forestry for Health and Well-Being

Focus has extended recently to the health benefits that trees in the city can bring. The Urban FWAC Network's Vision asserts that

> The urban forest will help address the health and wellbeing of our increasingly urbanized society (82% of people in England live in urban areas).

> Both physical and mental health will be improved, through: cleaner air (by removing and intercepting pollutants); reduced summer heating, reducing harmful effects of UV light and noise levels; access to green spaces for physical exercise that reduces stress, anxiety and mental fatigue.

Increasingly adaptation to climate change has become recognised as an important service to urban communities, through rainfall interception and storage, providing shade and reducing temperatures, as well as, in precise conditions, reducing air pollution. For example, Greater London's trees have been assessed as providing £133 million per year of air pollution reduction, stormwater attenuation and carbon sequestration, while Glasgow's trees intercept 812,000 cubic metres of rainfall per year – equivalent to £1.1 million in sewerage charges.

## Community Planting and the Big Tree Plant

Since the 1970s local people have become increasingly interested and involved in planting and maintaining trees and woods. This shift has happened from the ground up, with groups from schools, clubs, city farms, societies and parishes wanting simply to improve their own local environment by planting trees. Alongside the local groups, national organisations have thrived, providing training, support, funding and advocacy. The Conservation Volunteers, Tree Council, Trees for Cities and the Woodland Trust have worked with the Forestry Commission and other public bodies to facilitate and motivate local people. Communities have become increasingly important as both the customers and the consumers of forests, particularly in urban areas, and are essential partners in the Forestry Commission's work.

In England the government launched a tree planting scheme in 2010 to plant one million trees close to where people live and work. The Big Tree Plant was funded by the Forestry Commission and delivered in partnership with a host of others. Match-funding, almost pound for pound, came from community groups. A wide range of national bodies helped advise and supported delivery, while grant applications and payments were managed by Groundwork London. More than one million trees were planted, over two-thirds of which were in the most deprived and least green areas. In Birmingham, the Trees for Life project planted over 21,000 trees as part of the Big Tree Plant, involving schools, communities and local authorities. Volunteers in the Plymouth Tree Partnership planted over 10,000 trees, many along streets, to revitalise urban areas by working closely with the City Council and local community groups. The Long Buckby Green Space group in Northamptonshire planted 400 trees to enhance a park through the creation and maintenance of wildlife habitats, the growth of indigenous plants and trees, and improving the recreational use by schools, young people and the wider public through the provision of picnic areas, play areas and open spaces for camping.

Trees were mainly of native species, e.g. oak, field maple, rowan and alder (ash was also planted though curtailed by the emergence of Chalara dieback disease), and were planted as 1-metre-tall saplings. Larger specimen trees were planted in streets and prominent locations, and included varieties of cherry, sweet gum, lime and whitebeam. Orchard planting proved popular with schools and community groups. To mark the achievement of the target of one million trees, an English oak was planted by the Environment Secretary in Eastville Park, Bristol, accompanied by the mayor, the Chairman of the Forestry Commission and a host of enthusiastic schoolchildren.

## The i-Tree Eco Tool

As the value of urban forests has become recognised, so too has the need to gather detailed data on the state of the urban forests in our towns and cities. The i-Tree Eco tool, originally developed in the USA and adapted for use in the UK, has allowed cities to do this for the first time. It has been used to conduct surveys in towns and cities across Brtiain, supplying data on the structure and condition of each urban forest. By providing an economic valuation of their ecosystem services – including removal of air pollution, carbon sequestration and reducing the water entering drains – it also helps to promote their value: in Edinburgh, the ecosystem services of the urban forest were valued at £1.82 million per year and the carbon stored in its trees was estimated at 179,000 tonnes. The surveys have also revealed important details about the structure of our urban forests, including tree size diversity, tree cover and number of species. They have highlighted the lack of species diversity in many cities and therefore vulnerability to pests and diseases: ten key species make up 60–75 per cent of the total tree population in some of the surveyed areas, including Glasgow, Wrexham and Bridgend. By surveying both public and private trees, the ratio of which varies greatly between cities (e.g. 24–35 per cent private in Glasgow and Wrexham; 71–75 per cent in Torbay and Edinburgh), i-Tree has also emphasised the necessity for citywide forest management plans and for working with private as well as public owners. The results of the surveys are making a real difference: following its i-Tree survey in 2013, Wrexham Borough Council published a revised ten-year Tree and Woodland Strategy in 2016, which includes objectives such as 'urban tree canopy cover of 20% by 2026' and 'a tree population that is healthy, varied in age and diverse in species'.

In addition to individual i-Tree surveys, Forest Research, in partnership with Trees for Cities and Brillianto, have embarked on a project to map out the canopy cover of Britain's towns and cities. Recent research has estimated canopy cover in 283 English towns and cities at 15.8 per cent. The project aims to extend this to areas in Wales and Scotland, and also to get more detailed data down to ward level, which will help to identify which areas within a town or city would benefit most from future planting.

...........................................................................................................................................

# At 100 Years

Through a mix of intuition and common sense, pragmatism, science and philanthropy, people have created the urban forests we see today. They also seek to extend, improve and invest in these forests for the greater well-being of an increasingly urban world. By 2030 over 90 per cent of Britons will live in urban areas, and cities will need to invest in infrastructure of all sorts to cope with growth. Green infrastructure, parks, water, open spaces and urban forest will be essential to our future health and prosperity. Many party-political manifestos today include commitments on urban forestry as well as timber production. Ministers in all administrations take a close interest in urban forestry, adopting policies as part of wider social and economic development. Today, the Forestry Commission's work is delivered through different structures and governance across England, Scotland and Wales. As part of government it is guided by the policies of different administrations. The Commission's role in helping expand urban trees, woods and Community Forests has been significant and the legacy of this work will doubtless continue, shaped to suit political, economic and local demands. The roles of urban trees and woods are increasingly recognised, understood and valued. The Forestry Commission's remit has changed unrecognisably over its 100 years and urban and community forestry, while relative newcomers to the fold, will have some of the greatest impacts on the lives of millions of people and the communities in which they live and work.

# PART THREE: THE NATIONS' FORESTS

From Sutherland to Cornwall, from Suffolk to Carmarthenshire, the public forests of England, Scotland and Wales are blessed with extraordinary richness and diversity. While much of the rare and precious wildlife may elude all but the most fortunate or patient visitor, the ancient oaks and limes and the majestic pines and firs stand in the forest for all to enjoy. From medieval warrens to industrial tramways and Victorian arboreta, the legacy of the past is preserved in the forest, and from new urban greenspace to treetop walkways the infrastructure of contemporary human activity is also settling into the landscape.

The woodlands highlighted in this final section are only a selection of the more than two thousand that make up the forests of the three nations. They include some of the largest and most famous, as well as some smaller and less well known woods, remarkable for other reasons such as the particular species to which they play host. Inevitably many much-loved woods have had to be omitted, but taken together this collection gives a good representation of all that British forests have to offer.

# North of England

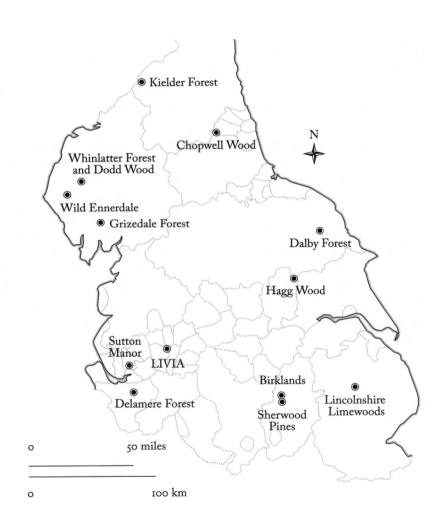

Kielder Forest

Chopwell Wood

N

Whinlatter Forest
and Dodd Wood

Wild Ennerdale

Grizedale Forest

Dalby Forest

Hagg Wood

Sutton
Manor

LIVIA

Birklands

Lincolnshire
Limewoods

Delamere Forest

Sherwood
Pines

o        50 miles

o        100 km

# Wild Ennerdale                                              4,400 ha

**Spectacular upland landscape of mountains, rock outcrops, extensive woodland, dynamic natural rivers, a glacial lake, and highly valued flora and fauna**

*Red squirrel, peregrine falcon, marsh fritillary, Arctic char, free-roaming cattle*

Lying on the western edge of Cumbria, Ennerdale is home to some of England's most vibrant natural environments and one of the longest-running wild land restoration partnerships in the UK. There is a sense of tranquillity, self-will and wildness, reminiscent of Scotland or Scandinavia. The forest feels vast, covering the valley floor – which has been shaped by the river Liza – and lower slopes. It is increasingly more species-diverse, helped by natural regeneration and planting of juniper, oak and mountain willows. Free-roaming forest cattle are pioneering new ways of farming. The high mountains are botanically rich with plants such as mountain eyebright and starry saxifrage. Ennerdale is considered to be the best example of a settled medieval valley in the Lake District.

# Grizedale Forest                                           2,447 ha

**Known as the premier forest for sculpture in Great Britain; made up of hills, tarns, and beautiful broadleaf and conifer woodland**

*Red kite, the only remaining indigenous red deer herd in England, red squirrel, roe deer, badger, rare white-faced darter dragonfly*

Located between Lake Windermere and Coniston Water, Grizedale Forest nestles in the heart of the World Heritage site within the Lake District National Park and is a wonderful interplay between open space, bodies of water, and broadleaf and conifer woodland. As the 'first forest for sculpture' (see pp. 183–7), Grizedale hosts over 40 sculptures which connect perfectly with the forest setting: sitting together in harmony, each tells its own story while contributing to the story of the other. The landscape adds a unique element, encouraging the viewer to question the relationship between sculpture and setting. Grizedale is also a home for adventure activities ranging from Go Ape zip trekking to gentle walks along the many waymarked trails.

## Kielder Forest                                                 59,187 ha

**Predominantly coniferous forest and open moorland, mainly in Northumberland although crossing into Cumbria**

*Hen harrier, osprey, red squirrel, goshawk, water vole*

Kielder Forest is a nationally significant forest, providing nearly half of the FC's timber production in England. Internationally important mires have now largely been restored, and large areas of riparian corridors of native woodland and open space have been created. Species diversity has been significantly improved as the forest is made more resilient and virtually all the British birds of prey, notably goshawks, have returned to the forest over the last 30 years. The natural return of the osprey has been enhanced by the provision of artificial nest platforms across the forest, which also boasts the biggest remaining population of red squirrels in England. Kielder is the perfect spot for stargazing and in 2013 became an internationally recognised Dark Sky Park (see pp. 191–2). Many woodland species such as birds, bats and moths have benefited greatly from the reduced light pollution in the forest.

## Whinlatter Forest and Dodd Wood                       1,512 ha

**Located either side of Bassenthwaite Lake in dramatic mountain landscape, offering stunning views of the Lake District**

*Osprey, red squirrel, roe deer, stag's horn clubmoss, bilberry*

Whinlatter Forest is England's only mountain forest and traces its history to the first year of the FC's plantings in 1919. The early trees, now tall and majestic, provide the backdrop to the experience of adventure and wildlife for the 250,000 visitors each year who come seeking peace, tranquillity and adventure.

The viewing platform in Dodd Wood provides fantastic views of the Bassenthwaite ospreys that have nested on the marsh each summer since 2001, becoming the first to breed in the Lake District for over 150 years. This was the result of several years' hard work by the Lake District Osprey Project – a partnership between the FC, Lake District National Park, RSPB and many dedicated volunteers. Dodd Wood has been at the forefront of forest landscaping and the developing practice of CCF management where regular thinning of the forest encourages diversity and natural regeneration.

## Chopwell Wood                                                   360 ha

**Mixed woodland on an ancient woodland site, set on the fringe of Gateshead, offering the largest woodland green space in Tyne and Wear**

*Red kite, great crested newt, badger, roe deer, wood ant, otter*

Chopwell Wood has a rich cultural heritage befitting an ancient woodland with close proximity to large settlements and communities. During the Second World War, Lumberjills managed the forest, operating a working sawmill producing timber products. Many of the old industrial tracks are used to support recreational activities. Today forest management mainly supports restoring the ancient woodland, with strong community involvement from the Friends of Chopwell Wood, while still producing significant amounts of timber for the wider economy. The wood is also a fantastic habitat for spotting wildlife. At the Bird of Prey viewpoint you may see red kites soaring over the picturesque backdrop of the Derwent Valley. These spectacular birds were re-released in 2004 after being absent from the region for over 50 years.

# Dalby Forest 3,575 ha

**Large area of varied woodland; mostly secondary plantation conifer forest, consisting primarily of spruce, larch and pine, with an increasing proportion of broadleaf and other conifer species**

*Nightjar, turtle dove, goshawk, barred green colonel soldier fly, yellow bird's-nest*

Acquired by the FC in 1921, Dalby Forest was one of the first sites which it planted. Workers were housed in prefabricated steel structures known as Nissen huts. To mark the FC's centenary, Rachel Whiteread created a concrete cast of one of these huts in the heart of the forest (see p. 198). Members of the Women's Timber Corps who were stationed here during the Second World War are also commemorated with a statue. Today Dalby is one of the largest areas of productive woodland in the North York Moors, allowing the FC to explore a range of silvicultural options. The steep terrain of the forest makes it perfect for mountain biking and Dalby has one of the best trail networks in the UK, including the World Cup Trail, which hosted the Union Cycliste Internationale Mountain Bike Cross Country World Cup for the first time in 2010.

# Hagg Wood 81 ha

**Mostly ancient woodland site with 1940s–60s plantation pine, oak and beech**

*Fragrant agrimony, lady's mantle, marsh tit, willow tit, lesser redpoll*

Hagg Wood is a PAWS area to the east of Dunnington, near York. It was established as a Community Woodland in 2003 with the long-term objective of restoring it as native semi-natural woodland, including oak, ash and other broadleaved trees and native woodland shrubs, as well as maintaining some of the larger conifers. The Friends of Hagg Wood preserve, protect and enhance the natural plant and animal life in the wood for the community, holding monthly conservation working parties as well as illustrated talks, social events and visits to places of conservation interest. The group is representative of the many other community groups to be found in Britain where public altruism and a love of nature brings together neighbours, friends and strangers to care for their local wood.

## Sutton Manor                                                    62 ha

**Former colliery pit near St Helens which is now urban woodland, home of *Dream***

*Roe deer, kestrel, bee orchid, water vole, kingfisher*

Sutton Manor was mined until the 1990s and leased to the FC in 2001 as part of a growing portfolio of Community Woodland in Manchester and Merseyside. After consultation with the local community, including many ex-miners, a project began to transform the site. Today, it boasts a mix of open grassland and mixed woodland, as well as a network of ponds and ditches which provide valuable habitats for wildlife, although there are still signs of the site's mining past, including capped mine heads. In 2005 the ex-miners put forward the site as a location for an iconic arts installation as part of Channel 4's *The Big Art Project* and as a result the site is home to *Dream*, a 20m-high sculpture of a young girl's elongated face by Spanish artist Jaume Plensa (see p. 194).

## LIVIA                                                          199 ha

**Urban forest oasis in north Manchester, close to the city**

*Roe deer, kingfisher, dragonfly, sparrowhawk, heron*

The Lower Irwell Valley Improvement Area (LIVIA) is a previously derelict site showing the remains of sewage works, lead works, a colliery and other heavy industry that put Manchester at the heart of the Industrial Revolution. The FC got involved with LIVIA forest in 2007

Newlands Programme, which brought together various egenerate brownfield sites. The woodland is a mix of old and new plantation, mainly broadleaf, and is home to a working coppice area. Many historical features still exist, including the base of the Irwell House and the 13 Arches railway viaduct. The FC continues to oversee the management of LIVIA and it is a source of pride to see it bursting with promise and used by local residents. What was previously an eyesore now adds great value to the neighbourhood.

## Delamere Forest                                            972 ha

**Largest wooded area in Cheshire, a mix of conifer and broadleaf**

*Large Mediterranean gull colony, white-faced darter dragonfly,* Sitticus floricola *(a rare jumping spider), round-leaved sundew (carnivorous plant), green hairstreak butterfly*

Delamere (Forest of the Lakes) sits on the Cheshire Plain near Frodsham, nestled between the major conurbations of Manchester, Liverpool and Chester. Managed by the FC since 1924, it is all that remains of the ancient Norman hunting forests of Mara and Mondrem. The forest (predominantly pine, with strips of broadleaves) includes meres and mosses. These wetland habitats have developed in kettle holes (depressions created as part of past glaciation) and have very diverse habitats and associated wildlife such as dragonflies, including the rare white-faced darter which was reintroduced to the forest by Cheshire Wildlife Trust and other partners in 2014. The Sandstone ridge looms over the forest and you can easily move along to the Eddisbury Hillfort, which dates to the early Bronze Age.

# Sherwood Pines 1,175 ha

**Largest area of woodland open to the public in the East Midlands; plantation forest with a range of habitats**

*Nightjar, goshawk, lizard, glow-worm, dark-green fritillary*

Originally called Clipstone Heath, Sherwood Pines was acquired and planted by the FC in 1925. The site provides valuable habitats for the nightjar, a rare bird which migrates to the UK in the summer to breed. Forest clearings, young plantations and heathland provide perfect nesting sites for this elusive species and recent conservation efforts have seen the population rise. Almost completely camouflaged during the day, nightjars are best spotted at dusk when visitors may be lucky enough to hear the male's churring song or spot one silhouetted against the sky searching for insects. The forest visitor hub includes a café, cycle shop, bike hire and high ropes courses. There are also extensive walking and cycling trails. Sherwood Pines also provides a significant supply of timber for local markets.

# Birklands 587 ha

**Remnant of the historic Sherwood Forest, consisting of oak-birch woodland with heathland, important in supporting a wide range of rare species**

*Nightjar, oak polypore (fungus), Welsh clearwing, slow-worm, bat*

The site is split into two distinct areas, one endowed with numerous ancient oaks within an SSSI and the other dominated by pine plantations. The forest provides evidence of over 1,000 years of activity: ancient oaks and old trackways survive from the era of the Royal Forest; broad rides through the forest and organised plantations remind us of a time when the local dukes managed it for profit and pleasure; banks and trenches tell of the military presence during and after the Second World War. The assembly site of Thynghowe on the western edge of Birklands dates back to the Vikings and local folk were still meeting here 200 years ago – a tradition recently revived by the Friends of Thynghowe who have been instrumental in investigating and researching the archaeology of the woodland and helping to protect it.

## Lincolnshire Limewoods                                          1,214 ha

**Mosaic of differing woodlands and habitat types, including a number of SSSIs**

*Brown hairstreak butterfly, barbastelle bat, nuthatch, dormouse, meadow thistle*

Lincolnshire is home to Britain's biggest concentration of traditionally managed small-leaved lime woodland, dating back over 10,000 years. The Limewoods consist of ASNW, broadleaf, mixed and conifer plantations; ponds, water courses, meadows and grass rides are a feature along with a large amount of important woodland edge habitat. Plants such as wood anemone, and rare butterflies such as the white admiral, are flourishing due to coppice management and the creation of open, sunny routes. There is little light pollution, making it a good place for stargazing, and Star Nights take place throughout the year. Work in the Limewoods is carried out in many ways from commercial standing sales to voluntary work via an array of partnership organisations. Armed with bill hooks, binoculars, cameras and notebooks, the volunteers help to monitor and record the vast and diverse array of woodland species in the Limewoods.

# Midlands

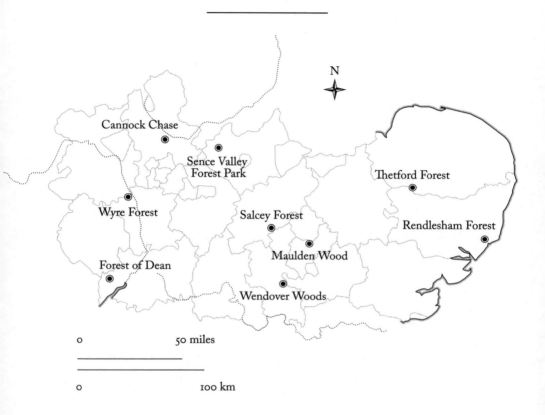

N

Cannock Chase

Sence Valley
Forest Park

Thetford Forest

Wyre Forest

Salcey Forest

Rendlesham Forest

Maulden Wood

Forest of Dean

Wendover Woods

| 0 | 50 miles |
|---|---|

| 0 | 100 km |
|---|---|

## Cannock Chase                                                    2,684 ha

**Predominantly secondary woodland, with a small area of ancient woodland, wood pasture and open heathland**

*800 fallow deer, Cannock berry* (Vaccinium intermedium), *skylark, nightjar, otter, water vole*

At the time of the Domesday Book (1086), the Chase was a Royal Forest known as Cank Forest; the wild deer roaming today are probably descended from the original herd introduced in Norman times. The forest lies within the Cannock Chase AONB and is home to rare and endangered species and habitats, including heathland which becomes covered in a purple blanket of heather in the summer months and a species of berry (*Vaccinium intermedium*) unique to the area. During the two world wars, significant areas of Cannock Chase were used as a training camp and the resulting military remains include a First World War model trench system at Brocton which is a Scheduled Monument. Cannock Chase is the biggest tourist attraction for outdoor pursuits within Staffordshire and surrounding areas.

## Sence Valley Forest Park (part of the National Forest)                                       111 ha

**63 ha of secondary woodland planted in 1998; plus 48 ha of open ground to be planted in 2019 as the FC's flagship Centenary Woodland**

*Otter, sand martin, kingfisher, bee orchid, Daubenton's bat, barn owl*

Sence Valley was once part of an opencast coal mine, reputedly the largest in northern Europe. In 1996 Leicestershire County Council acquired 63 ha of the site and transformed it into Sence Valley Forest Park, planting 98,000 productive coniferous and broadleaved trees, and creating grassland meadows and a series of lakes linked by the river Sence. Local volunteers assist the FC in managing the forest as well as undertaking practical conservation tasks including managing the artificial sand-martin wall. In 2018 the FC purchased a neighbouring area of the old mine for the national flagship planting site to celebrate the FC's Centenary in 2019. This new area will be planted during the winter of 2019/20 to create a mixed woodland of eight conifer and ten broadleaved tree species to produce a future forest resilient to the impact of pests, diseases and climate change. Grassed and surfaced trails will expand the area of public access land for walkers and cyclists to enjoy as the woodland develops, incorporating seasonal ponds and wildflower meadows. Unique features will also include a Centenary Avenue planted with five species of cherries to provide all-round colour and textures, and a community orchard of mixed fruit trees. Opportunities will be provided for local schools and communities to get involved with tree planting, hedge laying and creating a wildflower meadow adjacent to the river Sence.

## Salcey Forest 479 ha

**Ancient woodland site with oak trees dating from the 19th century, mixed with other broadleaves and post-war pine and spruce plantations**

*Wood white butterfly, crossbill, great crested newt, oval sedge, lesser spotted woodpecker*

Salcey Forest has a history of active woodland management dating back to its two Iron Age forts, when much of the woodland would have been coppiced for charcoal. William the Conqueror designated it a Royal forest to prevent further deforestation and gain control of timber and game. The forest is home to the rare Salcey 'druids' – veteran oak trees, some of which are believed to be over 500 years old. One of the most famous is the Milking Oak, so-called because milkmaids used to milk the cattle that grazed at Salcey Forest under its shade. During the Second World War, elephants from a travelling circus were used to pull felled trees out of the forest, after which they would cool down in what is now known as the Elephant Pond. The woodland now hosts around 250,000 visits each year.

# Wyre Forest 1,654 ha

**Remnant of the tract of ancient woodland covering much of south Shropshire, south-west Staffordshire and north Worcestershire**

*Wood warbler, tree pipit, skylark, adder, polecat, pearl-bordered fritillary*

Lying on an undulating plateau rising from the Severn Valley, Wyre Forest is one of the few which retains the mixture of woodland and grassland typical of most British medieval forests. The economic importance of oak coppice transformed the forest between the 16th and 19th centuries, leading to a predominance of oak today. Wyre is now managed by thinning, selective felling, and clear-fell/restock to increase the diversity of tree species characteristic of the ancient woodland. Due to the outstanding variety of habitat within Wyre, 1,094 ha are designated SSSI and a large part is designated as NNR. The diverse habitats – such as lowland mixed broadleaf woodland, lowland heathland, neutral grassland and streamside – support a large assemblage of birds, mammals, reptiles and invertebrates as well as a wide range of plant life and fungi, including nationally and locally scarce species, such as narrow-leaved helleborine and violet webcap.

# Forest of Dean Approx. 10,000 ha

**The Foresters' Forest, sitting between the rivers Wye and Severn in the westernmost part of Gloucestershire**

*Small pearl-bordered fritillary (last population in Gloucestershire), goshawk, peregrine falcon, hawfinch, great grey shrike, grizzled and dingy skipper butterflies, beaver*

The historic Forest of Dean has been protected for hunting and exploited for its mineral resource since Roman times. Among the many special characteristics of this extraordinary place are the ancient rights protected in statute such as those of the native born freeminers, the oaks planted to build the warships of the past, and a rich industrial heritage. In the

19th century the Darkhill Ironworks and the Titanic Steelworks played a critical role in the development of the technology to transform iron into steel; both sites are Scheduled Monuments and embedded in the woods. The Forestry Commission took stewardship of the Dean in 1924, and it became home to the first National Forestry Training School. In 1939 the Forest of Dean and Wye Valley woodlands were declared the first National Forest Park in England. The Forest is rich in wildlife, thriving on the mosaic of habitats that the woodlands encompass. Symonds Yat Rock, which has spectacular views of the river Wye, is a great place to see the peregrine falcons that nest on the limestone crags. The Forest is also home to a pair of Eurasian beavers, released into an enclosure in 2018 with the intention of reducing flood risk in the downstream village of Lydbrook. Known as ecosystems engineers, beavers can drastically modify their environment improving water quality and creating rich wetlands that store water.

## Maulden Woods                                                183 ha

**One of the largest remnants of ancient woodland in Bedfordshire, full of tracks and trails, and particularly important for wildlife**

*Hazel dormouse, adder, great-crested newt, white-letter hairstreak, wild daffodil*

This beautiful woodland is split into two distinct biogeographic zones, with the long-distance trail Greensand Way running between them. The northern half is mixed broadleaf woodland on brown earths, the southern half is Scots pine and heathland on sandy soils. It is the variety of soils that make the woodland so important. Maulden Woods was designated an SSSI in 1970 and supports an exceptionally rich invertebrate fauna, especially butterflies. It contains a significant number of hollow ways and wood banks, remnant of a rich history of use including during during the Second World War, and is still busy with walkers and riders, with several trails taking visitors to different walks throughout the woodland. Grassland rides are rich in wildflowers, including orchids, and there's a large wild service tree well worth a visit.

# Wendover Woods

325 ha

**Beautiful mixed forest with far-reaching views across the Chiltern Hills and Vale of Aylesbury**

*Firecrest, red kite, glow-worm, crossbill, earthstar fungus*

Wendover Woods is a wonderful local resource for visitors, located in the Chilterns AONB. Rising from 150m to 267m above sea level, the stunning forest drive takes visitors up through woodland before reaching the heart of the woods; a cairn marks the highest point in the Chiltern Hills. Over 50% of the wood is ancient woodland and is ecologically important as a local wildlife site. Bird species are diverse and include the rare migratory firecrest, which nests in the tall Norway spruce which provides it with a rich source of insect food. The wood's most popular trail, the Firecrest Trail, takes visitors through areas where this tiny bird can be seen. Wendover is also one of the best places to see magnificent red kites, once driven to extinction in England, but reintroduced to the Chilterns in 1989–94 where they are now thriving. The intriguing historic landscape includes an Iron Age hillfort on Boddington Hill, old paths and trackways, and Grim's ditch.

# Thetford Forest

Almost 19,000 ha

**Open-access forest landscape where dry pine plantations and pockets of lowland heath are interwoven with belts of shady broadleaves and lush river valleys**

*Woodlark, nightjar, military orchid, lesser spotted woodpecker, perennial knawel*

Thetford Forest was one of the largest areas to be planted by the FC following the First World War, overcoming extreme conditions and a harsh climate. It is now Britain's largest 'man-made' pine forest and continues to provide the nation with large quantities of timber.

Hidden among the trees are miles of earth banks – relics of an era when rabbits were farmed for meat and fur. Today their descendants roam wild, presenting a challenge to the foresters as they devour newly planted trees. Thetford Forest is internationally protected for its populations of woodlark and nightjar which nest in the felled and open areas. The network of sandy rides provides refuge for some of Britain's rarest small plants and insects, and the forest is nationally protected as an SSSI. Thetford has also become the venue for many amazing Forest Live concerts held every summer (see p. 88).

## Rendlesham Forest                                              1,425 ha

**Large conifer-dominated forest, prominent in predominantly low-lying landscape within the Suffolk Coast and Heaths NCA and AONB**

*Woodlark, nightjar, adder, silver-studded blue butterfly, moss stonecrop*

The great storm of 1987 with winds gusting up to 100mph flattened much of Rendlesham Forest. Fallen trees were preserved at Lynford Water using a pump that kept the timber wet to avoid degradation and swamping the market. Populations of woodlark and nightjar soared during this period, which – although a positive consequence for nature – is an unsustainable provision of habitat. Consequently there has been a reduction in harvesting in order to retain some mature trees and allow time for younger stands to grow. Opportunities were taken to re-landscape the forest area, introducing more broadleaf species and designing felling coupes with less square shapes to add visual diversity.

Rendlesham is a popular site for UFO enthusiasts after US Air Force personnel from nearby RAF Woodbridge reported seeing, and even touching, an alien spacecraft over a series of nights in 1980. This is commemorated with a 3-mile UFO trail and an interpretative model of the UFO in the forest.

# South of England

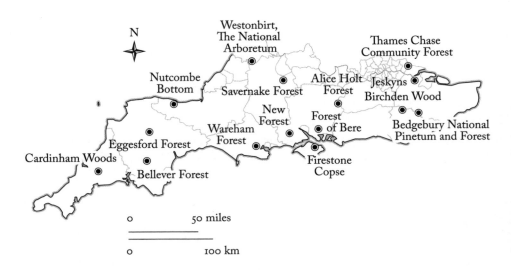

N

Westonbirt,
The National
Arboretum

Thames Chase
Community Forest

Nutcombe
Bottom

Savernake Forest

Alice Holt
Forest

Jeskyns

Birchden Wood

New
Forest

Forest
of Bere

Bedgebury National
Pinetum and Forest

Wareham
Forest

Eggesford Forest

Cardinham Woods

Bellever Forest

Firestone
Copse

0          50 miles

0          100 km

## Firestone Copse                                         98 ha

**Mixed woodland on the north-east of the Isle of Wight**

*Red squirrel, dormouse, Bechstein's bat (one of the UK's rarest), silver-washed fritillary and white admiral butterfly*

The whole of Firestone Copse is located within the Isle of Wight AONB and almost all is designated as PAWS. Notable trees include magnificent old oaks, young Corsican pines and western red cedars. Firestone Copse is one of the best places to spot red squirrels, as they skip from branch to branch among the trees while green woodpeckers peck away beneath them. Red squirrels make up the entire population of squirrels in the Isle of Wight but less than 140,000 of the total squirrel population of 2.5 million in the UK. The FC pays a key role in safeguarding these red squirrels, being careful to preserve and establish woodlands which encourage them to settle and breed. Since one of their favourite foods is pine cones, this includes planting conifer trees such as the Corsican pines which can be seen in Firestone Copse. The ground flora and scrub layer of woodlands across the Isle of Wight is particularly rich due to the long absence of deer.

# Forest of Bere - West Walk and Creech Woods

359 ha (West Walk); 181 ha (Creech Woods)

**West Walk is a beautiful ancient woodland – a mixture of woodland, heathland, farmland and downland; nearby, Creech Woods is a very old piece of woodland with veteran broadleaved trees and impressive Corsican pine trees planted in the 1960s**

*Dormouse, rare purple emperor butterfly (West Walk), bat, great crested newt*

West Walk and Creech Woods are among the few remaining fragments of the medieval Forest of Bere (from the Saxon 'Baer' meaning 'swine pasture'). The Normans made it one of their Royal forests where the king could hunt deer and wild boar.

West Walk is a prominent site for its small-leaved lime, a historically important species also likely to be well suited to our changing climate. A number of ponds provide valuable amphibian and reptile habitat.

Creech is known primarily for its impressive and statuesque conifers nestled snugly into the South Downs landscape, but is also home to a small number of broadleaves. The overall mix of tree species is of real silvicultural interest, and some areas of the woods provide good examples of CCF which significantly benefits woodland habitats.

# Alice Holt Forest                845.4 ha

## Located within the South Downs National Park, a mixture of ASNW and PAWS

*Grey heron, lesser spotted woodpecker, nightjar, willow tit, purple emperor butterfly, grass snake*

There has been a forest at Alice Holt since around 5000 BC when most of the trees were oaks and the woodland was much more extensive than today. From the Iron Age onwards, it was the site of a pottery industry, leaving it seriously depleted as the potteries required substantial amounts of wood to fuel the kilns. After centuries of deforestation followed by replanting, efforts today focus on restoring much of the lost native woodland, including gradually removing conifers within broadleaf woods and encouraging natural regeneration of native tree species. An arboretum created in Lodge Inclosure in the 1960s by researchers studying plant progeny and genetics is still popular with visitors today. Alice Holt Forest is also an exciting outdoor activity setting with improved facilities for visitors. A small part of the forest is designated as a nationally important SSSI for its wildlife, including the purple emperor butterfly – the emblem of Alice Holt; people travel from far and wide to see its courtship displays in high summer. Lucky visitors might also see a grass snake hunting for frogs in and around the forest's streams and ponds.

# New Forest

Almost 29,000 ha

**Beautiful SSSI of great historic and ecological importance in southern England**

*Dartford warbler, nightjar, curlew, bog orchid* (Hammarbya paludosa), *sand lizard*

One of our few remaining Royal forests, the New Forest was named by William the Conqueror and has been managed by the FC since 1924. It is a combination of heathland, ancient woodland, wetlands and grassy plains, with many inclosures of both coniferous and deciduous woodland. Commoning rights (the right to keep animals on the common areas, while abiding by certain regulations) have been preserved: ponies and other forest stock can be seen strolling around, while during the autumn pannage season many pigs are turned out to graze on acorns. The New Forest Verderers play an important role in protecting the traditions and landscape of the forest, and hold a regular court in the Queen's House in Lyndhurst.

The huge unfenced area known locally as Open Forest is one of the richest wildlife areas in Britain because it has such diverse habitats and is home to many species that are rare or absent elsewhere. There are about 1,000 ancient trees in the New Forest, which is the highest concentration in Western Europe. An incredible 63% of our 24,000 types of insects, 75% of all dragonfly species, and all six species of our native reptiles live here – including the adder, our only venomous snake. It is also an essential habitat for rare birds, including the Dartford warbler and other ground-nesting birds such as nightjars. The New Forest contains most of the remaining areas of lowland valley mires (better known as bogs) in Europe which have great conservation value. They are filled with plants such as aromatic bog myrtle with its fantastic balmy smell and uncommon species like the bog orchid and pale green sphagnum bog moss.

# Wareham Forest                                    1,542 ha

**Open heathland with a mosaic of woodland, west of Poole Harbour between Wareham and Bere Regis**

*Ladybird spider, woodlark, sand lizard, Dartford warbler*

The rugged landscape of Wareham Forest in Dorset is home to a rare and beautiful arachnid as small as a human fingertip: the ladybird spider. The adult males are the most impressive to look at with their bright red spotted backs, while the juvenile and female spiders are an unadorned black. The ladybird remains the rarest spider in Britain and until 2000 there were thought to be less than 100 in the UK due to the erosion of lowland heathland for agricultural and forestry purposes. Pioneering work by the FC to conserve the heathland, in partnership with other organisations and spearheaded by the preservation society Back from the Brink, has ensured that Wareham Forest has many of them hidden away in its lowland heathland. Because the spiders remain indoors for the majority of their time, the best time to spy a ladybird is in the spring when they can be found scurrying busily around.

# Westonbirt, The National Arboretum          240 ha

**Magical tree garden and internationally important botanical collection**

*Spreading bell flower (critically endangered), blue underwing moth, green-winged orchid, sooty-black smut fungus (v. rare), 13 species of bat*

The arboretum was the vision of the Victorian Robert Holford, who used his vast wealth to create a picturesque tree garden as an expression of his passion for plants and artistic design. The arboretum came into the care of the FC in 1956 which took on a broader range of objectives from plant conservation and scientific research to recreation and learning. In 2001 Westonbirt was awarded the status of National Arboretum with a mission 'to connect people with trees to improve the quality of life'. Today it is a Grade I Registered historic landscape of national significance and constitutes one of the world's finest collections of trees. The UK has only about 30 native tree species, whereas over 2,700 species and varieties can be found at Westonbirt; key examples include giant redwood (*Sequoiadendron giganteum*), one of our signature trees and some of the first to be planted here; a world-famous collection of 300 cultivars of Japanese maples (*Acer palmatum*); and the tallest and fattest Bristol whitebeam (*Sorbus bristoliensis*) in the country. The arboretum is also home to a rich variety of flowering plants, butterflies and 1,000 species of fungi. Management is actively supported by a Friends' charity with over 32,000 members. A six-year £7 million project has transformed the experience of the 500,000+ annual visitors, and includes the Stihl treetop walkway – the longest structure of its kind in the UK. The variety of trees makes for interest year-round with spring and autumn particularly colourful.

# Nutcombe Bottom                                                65 ha

### Historic Douglas fir plantation, home to England's tallest tree

*Red, fallow and roe deer, nightjar, bat, crossbill, tawny owl*

Situated on the edge of Exmoor National Park, within view of Dunkery Beacon, Nutcombe Bottom is a small pocket of tranquillity, providing a popular visitor destination within easy reach of the resort of Minehead. The highly favourable growing conditions produce fast-growing Douglas fir: the proximity of the meandering stream and free-draining soil are conducive to tall growth, while the sheltered position provides protection from wind damage. A special feature of Nutcombe is the Tall Trees Trail, an all-ability accessible route guiding visitors to England's tallest tree, a Douglas fir which has been growing on the site since 1876 and was 60.05 m when last measured in 2009. Its trunk weighs an estimated 50 tonnes with a diameter of 1.74 m. Nutcombe Bottom was acquired by the FC in 2017 and will be managed as the focal point for visitors for recreation within the Croydon Forest Plan and incorporated into the updated Exmoor Forest Plan.

## Savernake Forest 1,187 ha

**Famous for its majestic veteran trees and former wood pasture**

*Barbastelle bat, great crested newt, dormouse, red kite, nightjar*

Savernake Forest sits within the North Wessex Downs AONB. Most of the forest is an SSSI and much of the woodland lies within a Grade II site on the English Heritage Register of Historic Parks and Gardens. Leased to the FC in 1939, Savernake Forest includes some of the oldest trees in Europe: the Big Belly Oak took root around the time William the Conqueror defeated Harold in 1066, while the King of Limbs is a pollarded oak thought to be 1,000 years old and inspired Radiohead's album of the same name. Throughout the woodland, more than 6,000 ancient and veteran trees help to support a rich population of invertebrates, including moths, butterflies and spiders; many are reliant on the forest's high level of standing and fallen deadwood. Management practices are focused on maintaining the health and longevity of the veteran trees. A number of them have been 'haloed', which involves removing the surrounding trees to help maintain the veterans' vigour.

## Flashdown Wood, in Eggesford Forest 33 ha

**Mainly conifer plantation for commercial timber with some mixed broadleaved components**

*Hobby, goshawk, raven, dormouse, badger*

Flashdown Wood, sitting within Eggesford Forest, was acquired by the FC after the First World War and became well known within forestry circles as the place the very first tree planting took place. The original planting site is still visited regularly, and now enjoys the company of the FC's 50th and 75th anniversary commemorative trees, with a National Centenary tree avenue due to be planted in autumn 2019. Like the wider forest, Flashdown is mainly planted with coniferous species, grown for commercial timber. Douglas fir is predominant throughout, with Norway and Sitka spruces on the clay and in damper valleys. These grow alongside an increasing number of native broadleaves, including ash, sweet chestnut and oak. On the slopes of mid-Devon, Flashdown quietly weathers the decades, keeping safe the heart of the FC's legacy.

# Bellever Forest                                400 ha

**Majestic Sitka spruce plantation in the heart of Dartmoor National Park**

*Dartmoor pony, long-eared owl, goshawk, sparrowhawk, nightjar, small pearl-bordered fritillary*

Managed by the FC since 1931, Bellever was intended to be the centre of a much larger tract of upland forestry, but the planting plan was truncated as the importance of the moorland habitat to the nation took prominence. Home to Bellever Tor (an SSSI), numerous Scheduled Monuments and protected Dartmoor ponies, Bellever Forest has a history, wildlife and geology rich enough to impress any visitor. As birds of prey wheel above the towering conifers, visitors can choose to meander along the edges of the East Dart river or hike to the windswept Bellever Tor for stunning panoramic views and a glimpse of the forest's Bronze Age legacy. The adventurous history enthusiast can even walk in the footsteps of former Bellever inhabitants along the Lych Way, also known as the Way of the Dead: a 12-mile trek to Lydford, the parish where occupants of ancient tenements were obliged to attend services and carry out funerals. The forest has produced more than 300,000 tonnes of timber for the construction industry and is predominantly planted with highly productive Sitka spruce.

# Cardinham Woods

265 ha

## History-rich mixed woodland nestling on fertile Cornish slopes

*Dormouse, river trout, salmon, pearl-bordered fritillary (incl. small)*

Extending across seven stream valleys which feed Cardinham Water (a tributary of the river Fowey), Cardinham Woods' fertile slopes produce 1000–2000m³ of timber each year. The majority is classified as ancient woodland, having been continuously wooded for centuries. While a fifth of the site comprises broadleaf species, the remaining areas are dominated by conifer planting, mainly Douglas fir. The management intention is to encourage natural regeneration of native broadleaf species and support diversification of the age structure and species composition of the site. The deep valley offers both shelter and breathtaking views in all seasons of the year, while the varied woodland supports a diverse assemblage of wildlife, including birds of prey, several species of deer and the scarce pearl-bordered fritillary. River trout and salmon are evident in the water courses, adding to its charm. Cardinham boasts many historic features including the Wheal Glynn lead and silver mine, charcoal platforms and ancient stone hedge banks across the woodland.

# Jeskyns

146 ha

## Multifunctional Community Woodland which opened in 2007

*Skylarks, dormice, corn bunting, turtle doves, badgers*

A flagship example of a Community Woodland, Jeskyns provides a wonderful green space for the local community. The landscape has been transformed with over 130,000 trees and shrubs planted, 50 ha wildflower meadow sown, 8 km of new hedgerow, four new ponds, and even orchards with over 2,700 fruit trees of almost 800 varieties. Visitor numbers have risen to 330,000 a year as the site has matured, and people coming to this new and still developing woodland can benefit from 7 km of surfaced all-ability trails interconnected with 11 km of grass tracks, including a circular horse route and orienteering course. The local community has worked with the FC to establish the components of the woodland for everyone to enjoy long into the future and there is an ongoing community engagement programme running throughout the year led by on-site rangers, attracting a number of volunteers who contribute to site maintenance and conservation works.

## Thames Chase Community Forest Almost 400 ha

**Major pioneering regeneration initiative that saw the creation of 10 FC Community Woodlands on the edge of London**

*Water vole, green woodpecker, adder, great-crested newt, barn owl*

The Thames Chase Community Forest was created as part of a national programme in the 1990s. It spans east London and south-east Essex, occupies 104 km² and includes 48 different greenspace sites, of which the FC manages ten. Over the past 25 years the area has become an inspirational example of landscape regeneration – over 400,000 trees and shrubs have been planted in addition to 33 km of all-ability trails, family-friendly and mountain-bike trails, 12 km of dedicated horse trails, bird hides and play facilities for children across the FC sites. The sites provide a balance between recreational infrastructure for local communities and improved habitats to boost biodiversity. Thames Chase is still expanding as the FC continues to create new Community Woodlands on derelict landfill and quarry sites, increasing the myriad of benefits for people, nature and the economy.

# Birchden Wood                                    42 ha

**ASNW located on the East Sussex–Kent border within the High Weald AONB**

*Nightingale, common lizard, adder, slow-worms, digger wasp*

Since the Neolithic period, farmers have driven pigs onto the High Weald in autumn to feed on acorns. Their temporary camps were called dens, giving the forest its name, and their frequent passage wore away the soft soil, leaving sunken paths, one of which lies within the wood and has been used for over 6,000 years. The dense white-barked birch woodland we see today is the result of the 1987 storm which blew down many of the commercially planted conifers: the birches regenerated from the natural seed bank and the sandy soils provide perfect conditions for them. On sunny days common lizards can be seen sunbathing here; clearings and rides through the woods are regularly cut back to ensure that this continues. The wood is the main meeting point for a climb at Harrison's Rocks – a sandstone outcrop owned by the British Mountaineering Council – which lie on its western boundary. The Spa Valley Railway runs to the west of the site and steam trains can be seen and heard as they pass.

# Bedgebury National Pinetum and Forest

130 ha of pinetum, 850 ha of forest

**Unique rolling landscape, containing an incredible variety of conifers important on a global scale for species conservation and scientific advancement**

*Hawfinch, nightjar, brown long-eared bat, brilliant emerald damselfly, grizzled skipper butterfly, lemon-scented fern, colonies of common spotted orchid*

Bedgebury National Pinetum is one of the most impressive collections of conifers in the world. Bedgebury was founded in 1925 as a collaborative project between the FC and Royal Botanic Gardens, Kew. Bedgebury offered the acid, nutrient-poor soils that are ideal for a conifer collection plus an abundance of water in its streams and lakes. The mission since its inception has been to grow and maintain as many different species of conifer as possible. More than 1,800 different conifer and broadleaved species thrive here, including the critically endangered Sicilian fir of which there are only 29 mature specimens in its native range, and the Wollemi pine, a living fossil thought to be extinct but rediscovered in Australia in 1994. The collection itself and the continued conservation work of the Bedgebury team play a crucial role in the future of conifer trees. The landscape of the Pinetum is managed to create a variety of species-rich heath and acid grassland habitats to enable wild flowers, insects, birds and small mammals to live alongside the tree collection. Sweeping panoramic views of the tree collection and quiet benches off the beaten path allow visitors space and peace for artistic inspiration. Waymarked routes in the wider forest enable people to connect with trees through activities including walking, running, cycling, horse-riding and adventurous tree-top trails.

# Scotland

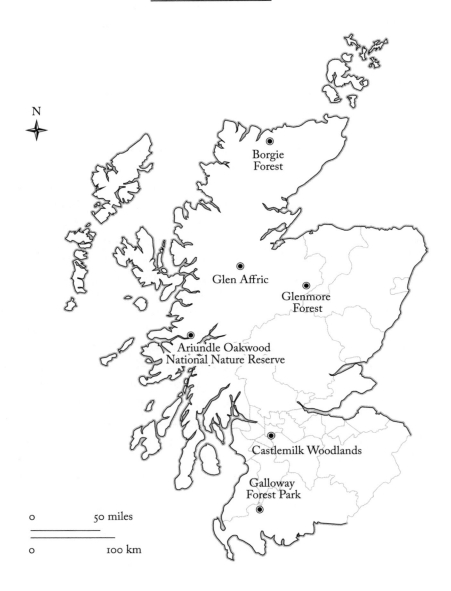

N

Borgie
Forest

Glen Affric

Glenmore
Forest

Ariundle Oakwood
National Nature Reserve

Castlemilk Woodlands

Galloway
Forest Park

| 0 | 50 miles |
| 0 | 100 km |

# Glenmore ('the Big Glen') Forest

3,500 ha

**Visitor hotspot lying at the foot of the Cairngorm mountains, with Loch Morlich and its famous sandy beaches at its heart**

*Capercaillie, pine marten, red squirrel, black grouse, crested tit*

Part of the largest remnant of Caledonian pine forest in Scotland, Glenmore Forest includes a diverse range of trees, from 300-year-old Scots pine to pioneer birch and juniper on the mountain slopes. It is also integral to the ambitious 200-year vision of the Cairngorms Connect Project, in which the RSPB, SNH, FES and Wildland Ltd aim to enhance habitats, species and ecological processes over an area of 600 km². Over time, the aim at Glenmore is to remove non-native conifers, regenerate or plant native species. and let the forest expand to a more natural treeline. As an NNR, the forest is also managed to benefit its huge variety of wildlife, thinning the forest to promote ground cover for capercaillie and keeping open areas that are important for rare bog species.

# Ariundle Oakwood National Nature Reserve

71 ha

**Oakwood on the northern side of Strontian Glen in the Sunart area of Lochaber**

*Chequered skipper butterfly, northern emerald dragonfly, otter, red deer, wildcat*

A precious and rare surviving fragment of an ancient oakwood that once spread along Europe's Atlantic edge from Spain and Portugal to Norway, Ariundle Oakwood is a habitat type that requires special protection. Along with similar woodlands surrounding Loch Sunart, it is part of Britain's largest continuous area of this type of oak woodland and consists mostly of sessile and pendunculate oaks and their hybrids, while also including other species such as birch, rowan and wych elm. A lush growth of primitive plants such as mosses, ferns and lichens covers the trees and the woodland floor, thriving in the mild and humid west coast climate. Ariundle is one of the best sites in Scotland to catch a glimpse of otter and, in the summer months, the rare chequered skipper butterfly and many species of dragonfly – including northern emerald dragonfly.

## Galloway Forest Park — 75,000 ha

**Large park, stretching from Arran to the Tweed Valley and beyond**

*Golden eagle, osprey, black grouse, nightjar, pine marten*

Galloway Forest Park accounts for more than half of the larger Galloway forest area. This, added to the fact that it is one contiguous area, makes it a very special place, ideal for projects on the grand scale. Predominantly a commercial coniferous forest that delivers over 600,000 tons of timber annually – much of it for the construction sector – Galloway Forest Park is becoming increasingly diverse as more broadleaf species are planted. Sparsely populated, its remoteness makes it a haven for wildlife, such as golden eagles, otters and other raptors. It is an ideal location for out-of-the-way adventure, including two wildlife parks (a red deer range and a wild goat park), two forest drives and over 150 miles of walking and mountain bike trails. It is Europe's first Dark Sky Park.

## Castlemilk Woodlands, Glasgow — 109 ha

**Mature woodland on the fringes of Scotland's biggest city**

*Bluebell, snowdrop, wood anemone, common spotted and northern marsh orchid*

Castlemilk Woodlands offers mature woodland, open spaces, and a network of paths that meander around the ruins of Castlemilk House which was demolished in 1969. Beginning life as a semi-natural woodland, non-native species were introduced in the 19th century. During the 1950s, Castlemilk was developed as a housing scheme to accommodate thousands of people from inner city areas such as the Gorbals. Over the years, social problems associated with poverty and unemployment grew and regeneration of the area began in 1980s, focusing on improving housing and the building of a sports centre, swimming pool and community centre. Nowadays the woodland is a welcome green space that attracts many people of all ages. Recreation and interpretation trails have been created and access improved in tandem with investment of over £2 million that has helped rejuvenate the area.

## Glen Affric Forest                                                    14,500 ha

**Classic landscape of perfectly placed lochs, mountains and a mix of pine, birch and oak trees**

*Golden eagle, black grouse, red deer, red squirrel, pine marten*

Glen Affric is one of the most beautiful places in Scotland. As Britain's largest area of pine forest that is close to being in its natural state, it is a wonderful place to get an impression of the Caledonian Forest that once covered much of Scotland, the glens thick with trees and more open woodland on the hills. It is unsuitable for commercial forestry because of its soil and ground, and more suited to native woodlands. The importance of these woodlands has latterly seen a resurgence and the focus of forest management has shifted to the removal of forest fencing and non-native trees. The Glen is part of a programme to reinstate a much wider area of Caledonian Forest and is also protected as an NNR since it is an important haven for wildllife. Deer management is important to ensure the healthy Caledonian pine forest continues to flourish.

## Borgie Forest, Sutherland                        6,325 ha

**Working forest that takes its name from the river Borgie, one Scotland's most famous salmon rivers, which flows through the forest**

*Salmon, red deer, buzzards, trout, otter, gorse*

Although one of the first forests planted by the FC in Scotland back in 1920, a devastating fire in the 1940s caused such damage that much of it had to be replanted. Those trees have now reached maturity and are ready to harvest, which will present the opportunity to plant a mix of broadleaves and native species to encourage and support a wide range of wildlife. Indeed, native trees are particularly important to local Gaelic-speaking people as each letter of the Gaelic alphabet is traditionally associated with a different tree. The few original trees that were unaffected by the fire and are still standing are now some of the tallest in Sutherland and located within Borgie Glen. Borgie is a working forest that also welcomes walkers, birdwatchers and many other visitors – in spring the flowering gorse is spectacular.

# Wales

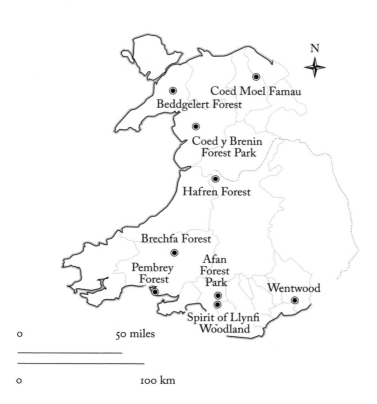

## Afan Forest Park                                                        3,940 ha

**Productive high forest situated north-east of Port Talbot, elevation 50–550 m, known for its mountain bike trails**

*Otter (on Afan river), heron, fallow deer, crossbill, nightjar, buzzard*

The forests and woodlands of the Afan Valley have sprung from a land of scattered farmsteads, ancient woodlands, viaducts, disused railways and coal-mined land. The FC planted most of the forest area with conifers

257

in the 1950s–60s with further planting in the 1980s: larch and pine were planted on the lower slopes and spruce on the upper slopes. The first recorded outbreak of *Phytophthora ramorum* (see p. 180) in larch in Wales was recorded in the Afan Valley and over 15% of the forest area has had to be felled over the last eight years, giving NRW an opportunity to create a robust and resilient forest with a wider range of trees: about one-third will be broad-leaved and the remainder coniferous. The FC designated this area as Afan Forest Park in 1972 because of its great walking potential: waymarked walks and bridleways lead to some breathtaking viewpoints. Afan is also known across the world for its world-class mountain-bike trails.

# Beddgelert Forest                                        700 ha

**Mainly upland conifer forest**

*Goshawk, common and soprano pipistrelle, palmate newt, otter, damsonfly*

Beddgelert consists of a rocky ridge on the flanks of Moel Hebog to the south-west of the central Snowdon massif within Snowdonia National Park. In 1927 the FC made the first plantings here on an old conifer woodland site containing remnants of Scots pine and European larch, and established an early set of research trials whose conclusions remain important today (see Part II, Chapters 1 and 3). The current management of this mainly productive conifer forest is to diversify the woodland species and increase the component of broadleaves, riparian woodland and open space to reflect the surrounding landscape. There is a wide range of wildlife species associated with upland woodland areas, including bats, and a number of bird species including raptors. In the wetter woodland areas there are otters, newts and damsonflies. Beddgelert enjoys high visitor numbers and includes a busy campsite and a public car park to enable access to a number of trails through the forest for walking, riding and mountain biking.

# Brechfa Forest

6,500 ha

## Productive high forest in the rural uplands of West Wales

*Fallow deer, otter, dormouse, pine marten (rare sightings), nightjar*

Brechfa Forest was one of the earliest forest creation schemes in the 1920s. The Women's Land Army of the 1940s was instrumental to its continued creation and management. Now in part in its third rotation, it is one of the European-designated forest gardens created during the 1950s and 1960s, with over 89 different species of exotic forest tree species, including the iconic redwoods of California, Serbian spruce and Chile pine. It is a wildlife haven, typical of many upland Welsh forests, and includes a fallow deer population. Birds of prey are now a dominant feature, following a successful reintroduction and promotion of their habitat by the FC during the 1990s. More recently Brechfa Forest has hosted motorsport, including the RAC rallies, now the Wales Rally GB. It also has one of the largest wind farm operations, with Innogy Renewables creating energy for over 38,800 homes in Carmarthenshire.

# Coed y Brenin Forest Park

3,500 ha

## A very productive forest carefully balanced with a recreation hub, biodiversity and some of the tallest trees in Wales.

*Freshwater pearl mussel, goldcrest, dipper, otter, dormouse*

Coed y Brenin was an exemplar of sustainable management of natural resources and delivery of multiple well-being benefits before this became a legislative requirement in Wales. The Afon Eden SAC located within the forest was the only Welsh location to be included in the Pearls in Peril project which worked to safeguard the future of freshwater pearl mussel populations in Britain. The forest has an average annual timber production of 22,000 m$^3$ (enough to build 12,570 timber-framed houses) which supports employment in the forestry sector and rural communities. Coed y Brenin is the first dedicated mountain bike centre with a hand-built, all-weather network of trails through the forest which now caters for everyone from families to world-class racers. The site includes a purpose-built visitor centre, opened in 2006 and extended in 2013, which had sustainable construction principles at its heart.

## Hafren Forest                                                     3,498 ha

**Upland forest close to the source of the rivers Severn and Wye**

*Nesting ospreys, crossbill, pine marten, goshawk, otter*

Hafren, which takes its name from the Welsh name for the river Severn, primarily functions as a commercial forest. It was created by the purchase of upland farms, and the earliest planting began in 1937. The Centre for Ecology and Hydrology has carried out water testing here for 30 years, which has been instrumental in creating UK Forest and Water Guidelines, recommendations on how to meet the UKFS requirements for water. The forest has interesting geology and was mined from the Bronze Age to the 19th century – features which are still studied today, including the mineralisation process and the Hafren drinking stone. Hafren was one of the first Welsh forests to develop a Forest Plan, with small coupes, diverse structure, species and managing water and landscape. The forest supports a range of typical forest birds, and in 2014 the fifth pair of Welsh breeding ospreys nested in Hafren. This has been a productive nest and a draw for wildlife enthusiasts. It also boasts a popular walk up cascading streams to the source of the River Severn and is the start of the Severn Way and Wye Valley Walk long-distance walks.

# Spirit of Llynfi Woodland 65 ha

**Mixed native broadleaf woodland, heathland, grassland and recreational areas including community fruit orchards**

*Skylark, lesser spotted woodpecker, common blue butterfly, slowworm, emperor dragonfly*

Lying along the eastern slopes of the Upper Llynfi Valley in South Wales, the woodland is currently owned by Bridgend County Borough Council and managed by NRW. A masterplan for the site was developed in partnership with the local community in spring 2015. Ranging from local schools to community groups, neighbourhood residents to volunteers from Ford Motor Co., the community planted over 7,000 trees, bringing the total number of trees planted on site to 60,000. The Spirit of Lynfi woodland project aims to use the natural environment as a catalyst for improved well-being and healthier, happier communities. Combining 30 ha of new woodland planting with various community-led initiatives has transformed a former colliery site into a dynamic community woodland, enabling people living in one of Wales's most deprived wards for health to access the countryside on their doorstep.

# Coed Moel Famau 428 ha

**Productive high forest and open space habitat, elevation 320–500 m**

*Black grouse, crossbill, raven, buzzard, great spotted woodpecker*

Situated in Denbighshire in north-east Wales, Coed Moel Famau sits within the Clwydian Range and Dee Valley AONB. The first planting was in 1949 with most of the remaining area planted by 1953. These early plantations were dominated by Japanese larch, Norway spruce and Sitka spruce. Now into its second rotation, approximately 50% of the forest is designated to LISS management with additional tree species present including Douglas fir, western red cedar and native broadleaves. The forest supports a good variety of wildlife including a healthy black grouse population. Sitting on the edge of Offa's Dyke National Trail, it also provides many recreational opportunities, including walking, mountain biking and a nature play trail. Coed Moel Famau continues to be managed jointly with the neighbouring Country Park through one of the most successful and long-standing partnerships of its kind in Wales.

## Pembrey Forest                                    1,000 ha

**Productive high forest within a once-mobile sand dune landscape towards the Irish Sea and Bristol Channel**

*Orchid, badger, variety of bat species, narrow mouthed whorl snail, jewel wasp*

Situated on Carmarthen Bay, Pembrey Forest is one of the few and earliest designated Conservation Forests of the FC in Wales and results from the creation of man-made sand dunes to slow down ever-encroaching coastal erosion. Now in part in its second rotation, it predominates as a Corsican pine forest whose timber is sought-after by sawmillers and telegraph-pole manufacturers, due to the excellent even growth and minimal rate of taper of the logs. Today's forest is a conservation-managed area and wildlife haven typical of a sand dune forest habitat, including numerous butterfly species along the butterfly forest ride systems within the forest, the rare tiny-mouthed whorl snail found in only five locations across the UK, and a wide variety of flora. The forest hosts iconic events such as Battle on the Beach and contributes to the local economy with Pembrey Conservation Trust, which offers training and work in the forest to those in long-term unemployment.

# Wentwood                                      660 ha

**Lowland productive high forest, with an elevation of 80–300 m**

*Long-eared bat, dingy skipper butterfly, firecrest, nightjar, dormouse*

Situated near Newport and overlooking both the Usk Valley SAC and the Severn Estuary Ramsar site, Wentwood is the largest area accorded ancient woodland status in Wales, confirmed by pollen analysis and historic mapping. It contains prehistoric hillforts later used by Roman invaders, and was a hunting preserve for Norman lords before passing into the Duke of Beaufort's estates. A 1730s map of the road from Monmouth to Cardiff identifies Wentwood with an unmistakeable conifer symbol. Acquired by the FC in the 1940s–50s, today Wentwood is stocked with 29 species, a little over 50% of which are broadleaf. The entire woodland is designated as LISS management, with CCF the objective by 2060. Sadly, *Phytophthora ramorum* is present (see p. 180), and sanitation clear-fells make a dramatic impact; however, restock with native broadleaves may accelerate efforts to restore ASNW in the medium to longer term.

# Abbreviations

AONB     Area of Outstanding Natural Beauty
ASNW     Ancient Semi-Natural Woodland
CCF     Continuous Cover Forestry
Defra     Department for Environment, Food and Rural Affairs
EPS     European Protected Species
ESC     Ecological Site Classification
FC     Forestry Commission
FCS     Forestry Commission Scotland
FES     Forest Enterprise Scotland
FR     Forest Research
FWAC     Forestry and Woodlands Advisory Committee
GIS     Geographic Information System
LISS     Low Impact Silvicultural Systems
NCA     National Character Area
NFI     National Forest Inventory
NGO     Non-Governmental Organisation
NNR     National Nature Reserve
NRW     Natural Resources Wales
PAWS     Plantation on Ancient Woodland Site
RDA     Regional Development Agencies
RSPB     Royal Society for the Protection of Birds
SAC     Special Area of Conservation
SNH     Scottish Natural Heritage
SSSI     Site of Special Scientific Interest
UKFS     United Kingdom Forestry Standard
WTC     Women's Timber Corps
YC     Yield Class

# Further Reading

Alfrey, N., Sleeman, J. & Tufnell, B. (2013) *Uncommon Ground: Land Art in Britain 1966-79.* Hayward Gallery Publishing.

Crowley, D. (2017) *Westonbirt Arboretum's Tree Spotter's Guide: The Definitive Guide to Britain's 100 Best Trees.* Ebury Press.

Cooper, A. (ed.) (2017) *Arboreal: A Collection of Words from the Woods.* Little Toller Books.

Dempsey, A. (2006) *Destination Art: Land Art / Site-Specific Art / Sculpture Parks.* Thames & Hudson.

Hemery, G. & Simblet, S. (2014) *The New Sylva: A Discourse of Forest and Orchard Trees for the Twenty-First Century.* Bloomsbury.

Foot, D. (2010) *Woods and People: Putting Forests on the Map.* The History Press.

Forestry Commission (2017) *The UK Forestry Standard.* Forestry Commission.

Johnston M. (2015) *Trees in Towns and Cities: A History of British Urban Arboriculture.* Windgather Press.

Leslie, R. (2014) *Forest Vision: Transforming the Forestry Commission.* New Environment Books.

Peterken, G. (2008) *Natural Woodland: Ecology and Conservation in Northern Temperate Regions.* Cambridge University Press.

Pringle, D. (1994) *The Forestry Commission: The First 75 Years.* Forestry Commission.

Rackham, O. (2001) *Trees & Woodland in the British Landscape: The Complete History of Britain's Trees, Woods & Hedgerows.* Phoenix Press.

Rackham, O. (2006) *Woodlands.* William Collins.

Reynolds, F. (2016) *The Fight for Beauty: Our Path to a Better Future.* Oneworld Publications.

Richards, E.G. (2003) *British Forestry in the 20th Century: Policy and Achievements.* Brill.

Ryle, G.B. (1969) *Forest Service: First Forty-Five Years of the Forestry Commission of Great Britain.* David & Charles.

Sandberg, L.A., Bardekjian, A. & Butt, S. (Eds.) (2014) *Urban Forests, Trees and Greenspace: A Political Ecology Perspective.* Routledge.

Stewart, M. (2016) *Voices of the Forest: A Social History of Scottish Forestry in the Twentieth Century.* John Donald Short Run Press.

Watkins, C. (2014) *Trees, Woods and Forests: A Social and Cultural History.* Reaktion Books.

Williams, M. (1994) *Lumber Jill: Her Story of Four Years in the Women's Timber Corps 1942-45.* Ex Libris Press.

Williamson, T., Barnes, G. and Pillatt, T. (2017) *Trees in England: Management and Disease since 1600.* University of Hertfordshire Press.

# Acknowledgements

I am proud to have brought together the knowledge and expertise of staff from across the Forestry Commission, both past and present, to tell the story of our first 100 years.

This book has been a truly collaborative effort. I would like to thank the following people for their expertise and time spent researching, writing and reviewing chapters throughout this publication:

*One Hundred Years:* Helen Connor-Walton and Louise Fleetwood, Katherine Deeks, Paddy Harrop, Richard Howe, PK Khaira-Creswell, Brian Mahony, Josh Roberts, Sir Henry Studholme, and Ruth Wilson.

*Among the Trees:* Gary Kerr and Bill Mason (Silviculture), Jonathan Spencer (Habitats), Peter Freer-Smith (Forest Science), Chris Quine (Forest Hazards), Hayley Skipper (Arts in the Forest) and Mark Durk (Cities).

*The Nations' Forests:* Forestry Commission colleagues too numerous to mention in all the districts of Forestry England, and our friends in Forestry and Land Scotland, Scottish Forestry and Natural Resources Wales.

For her enthusiasm, commitment and hard work to make the idea a reality I am especially grateful to Megan Shirley. Heartfelt thanks are also due to Sir Henry Studholme, PK Khaira-Creswell, Ruth Wilson and Hayley Skipper – the team who brought the whole project to life – and to Brian Mahony who reviewed multiple iterations of the manuscript and generously shared his time and knowledge.

I am indebted to Bedgebury Pinetum Florilegium Society for granting us permission to use their beautiful artwork to illustrate the book. The photographs all come from the Forestry Commission's own archives.

Thank you to Peter Jones at Profile Editions for the valuable insight and sensitive editing he brought to our manuscript, and to Caroline Clark whose design has brought our words to life.

Finally, thank you to all the people of the Forestry Commission, past and present. Today the threat of climate change and the pressures of a growing population make all that our forests give us – homes for our wildlife, timber for our own homes; trees to lock up carbon, woods to set our spirits free – more precious than ever. Without the people of the Forestry Commission, most of these forests would not exist. Their work, and their story, goes on.

*Ian Gambles*

# Index